Contents

The Health and Care of Older People in London

A report to the King's Fund London Commission

A. M. Warnes

Published by
King's Fund Publishing
11–13 Cavendish Square
London W1M 0AN

© King's Fund 1997

First published 1997

ISBN 1 85717 170 5

A CIP catalogue record for this book is available from the British Library

Distributed by Grantham Book Services Limited
Isaac Newton Way
Alma Park Industrial Estate
GRANTHAM
Lincolnshire
NG31 9SD

Tel: 01476 541 080
Fax: 01476 541 061

Printed and bound in Great Britain by
Biddles Limited, Guildford and Kng's Lynn

Cover photographs by Richard Bailey

Acknowledgements

It has been possible to prepare this report in a relatively short time only because substantial help and guidance have been enthusiastically given by many people. Particular thanks are due to Virginia Beardshaw and Seán Boyle of the London Commission for a very clear brief and helpful 'steers' throughout, and to Seán and Richard Hamblin for their imaginative suggestions on sources and analyses and the well-judged drip-feed of data they supplied. Richard also speeded the calculations, design and creation of the tables and figures. Richard Poxton enabled a running start by summarising the many substantial commissioned thematic papers, the authors of which are also thanked profusely. Nicola Delaney has provided excellent secretarial support. The project support group and the Commission have at short notice read interim drafts, provided detailed textual commentaries, and gathered by Cavendish Square to set me on straighter tracks. All assisted immensely but I made particular demands on Pearl Brown's, Richard Himsworth's and Jacqueline Morris's time. The Librarians at the King's Fund were delightfully helpful. Kate Smith in the Centre for Ageing and Rehabilitation Studies of ScHARR at the University of Sheffield has given her usual skilful support, particularly with the successive re-drafts.

Abbreviations and glossary

Borough	Refers to 32 of the 33 statutory local government authorities of London. The other is the City of London which governs the 'square-mile' but few residents.
CCP	Community care plan. Required by statute to be produced annually by local authority Social Service Departments with inputs from relevant providing agencies.
CHS	Community health care services (often applied to a NHS trust).
Dependency	In this report, nothing to do with drugs, but the dependency on others through ill-health or disability for performing the 'activities of daily living' such as dressing, eating, bathing or toileting *or* the 'instrumental activities of daily living' such as cooking, laundry, shopping and housework.
DH	Department of Health
DHA	District health authority
DSS	Department of Social Services
FCE	Finished consultant episode
FHS	Family health services, including general medical practice, general dental practice and pharmacies.
FHSA	Family health service authority. The planning and funding bodies for the family health services which succeeded family practitioner committees and in 1996 were merged into health authorities.
FPC	Family practitioner committee. See FHSA.
GHS	General Household Survey: a long-standing government national social survey currently under review.
GLC	Greater London County. Disbanded in 1986, but the geographical area continues as the territory of the 32 London boroughs.
GMS	General medical services, which are mainly delivered by general practitioners.
GP	General medical practitioner
GPFH	General practice fundholder
HA	Health authority
HALE	Healthy and active life expectancy
HAS	Health Advisory Service. Now merged into the Royal College of Psychiatrists Research Unit

HCHS	Hospital and community health services
HMSO	Her Majesty's Stationery Office
ICD	International classification of diseases of the World Health Organization
LLTI	Limiting long-term illness
LMA	The London Metropolitan Area, comprising London and the Outer Metropolitan Area (*q.v.*)
London	Refers in this report to the area of the erstwhile Greater London County (*q.v.*)
LRC	London Research Centre
Mid-year population estimate	An estimate of the population of an area produced by the ONS. It is based on the estimated resident population at the previous census adjusted from locally supplied information on changes to the housing stock and other sources on migration change (*e.g* the electoral register and NHS re-registration).
Nursing home	An institutional dwelling *either* owned and managed by a local government authority, a voluntary agency, a legally registered company or an independent proprietor and registered with a local authority *or* owned and managed by an NHS trust. Nursing homes are required to register with the local health authority under Part 2 of the Registered Homes Act 1984. The latter are subject to internal NHS 'registration and inspection'. To be distinguished from residential homes (although some establishments provide both levels of care).
OMA	Outer Metropolitan Area. An officially recognised statistical area, being a ring around London which extends beyond the London 'green belt' to include rapidly expanding Home Counties towns.
ONS	Office for National Statistics. See OPCS.
OPCS	Office of Population Censuses and Surveys. In April 1996 merged with the Central Statistical Office to become the Office for National Statistics.
Pensionable population	The population eligible for United Kingdom state retirement pensions in 1997, i.e. 65 years and more for men and 60 years and more for women.
Residential home	An institutional dwelling registered with a local authority social services department to provide residential care for older people or others. May be owned and managed by a local government authority, a voluntary agency, a legally registered company or an independent

	proprietor. Residential homes are registered with the local authority under the Residential Homes Act 1984. To be distinguished from a nursing home (although some establishments provide both levels of care).
RHA	Regional health authority. Now regions of the NHS Executive.
SMR	Standardised mortality ratio. An age-standardised method of comparing a schedule of death rates with the national schedule.
SSD	Social services department (of a local government authority).
SSI	Social Services Inspectorate
Voluntary agency	A charitable or other non-statutory or non-corporate body. References in this report are generally to agencies involved in the provision of services for older people or advocacy.

Summary

Population

- Greater London has over the last two decades become the English metropolitan area with the lowest share of its population in the older age groups. 18 per cent of its population is aged 60 years and over compared to 21 per cent in the rest of England. The older population of approaching 1.3 million is 14 per cent fewer than the national age structure would imply.

- The shortfall is mainly of people aged from their mid-60s to mid-70s and, in comparison to the rest of England, there are relatively large shares in the youngest and the oldest age groups of older people. In 1995 the average age of both men and women aged 65 years and over in London was higher than in England – and the differential had widened during the early 1990s.

- London's pensionable-age population is presently falling and decreases are likely to continue until the middle of the next decade, before a slight recovery to 1,003,000 in 2011. The number aged 85 years and over is likely to increase during the 1990s from 101,000 to 119,000, but to fall during the first decade of the next century by 5,000.

- Inner London's age structure has changed markedly in the last two decades, and its population is increasingly dominated by working-aged people. Twenty years ago outer London's population had a high share of older people but its relative senescence has declined quickly. It still has an over-representation of people aged 75 years and more.

- People approaching and passing through the age of retirement in London are unusually likely to move out of the city. The exodus is selective of owner-occupiers, middle and higher income groups and the White population. The net effect is to lower the socio-economic profile of those who remain.

- London has the highest proportion of minority ethnic older people of any region of the country. Rapid increases in the number of older people in the Black-Caribbean and Indian communities are now occurring. Black Caribbeans aged 60–74 years may decrease in number during the late 1990s in inner London while continuing to increase in outer London.

- The rate of increase of people aged 75 years and over in the minority ethnic communities will be very high during the next few decades but the total number, presently around 12,000, will not reach 20,000 for another decade.

- The Black-Caribbean older population is heavily concentrated in inner London boroughs, particularly Brent, Hackney, Haringey, Lambeth, Southwark and Lewisham. The Indian population is strongly clustered in outer London, one concentration overlapping the boroughs of Brent and Harrow, a second overlapping

Ealing and Hounslow, and the third being located on the borders of Newham and Redbridge. The much smaller Bangladeshi population is exceptionally concentrated in Tower Hamlets and has high rates of deprivation and sickness.

Health

- Substantial improvements in late-life mortality have been achieved in London (and the rest of England and Wales) in recent years, but the United Kingdom has done far less well than several neighbouring European countries. Comparisons with France, Switzerland or Spain indicate that there is much 'premature' morbidity and mortality in this country.

- Broadly the epidemiology of older people in London is similar to that elsewhere in the United Kingdom. The majority of those in their 60s and 70s are healthy, active and without disability. Levels of disability increase with age but remain a minority characteristic until the 80s. The incidence of acute clinical episodes increases from late middle-age, and rises sharply in the five years before death.

- The incidence of acute episodes increases with age from late middle-age and the most common outcome is recovery and recuperation. The majority of older people have health problems similar to those of other adults, and the majority of their contacts with the health services are little different to the presentations by the middle-aged.

- The minority with chronic and multiple disorders, mostly aged at least 75 years, require relatively intense medical and social care from the primary care, 'care of the elderly', community health, and domiciliary and residential social services and in nursing homes.

- On many standard measures of morbidity, perceived health and functional abilities, London's older population appears marginally better off than their counterparts in the rest of England (and therefore in the rest of the United Kingdom). Late age mortality rates from stroke and several cardiac disorders have been lower in London than elsewhere but the differentials are narrowing in middle-age.

- Remarkably, this advantage appears to extend to inner-deprived areas, where the reported female rates are lower than in high-status areas. Inaccurate estimates of the 'usually resident' population, particularly for the oldest ages and women, may distort the figures.

- The poorest health conditions among older people are found in the inner-deprived areas and among the more recently established minority ethnic groups, notably the Pakistanis and the Bangladeshis. There is an over-representation of men in the young elderly age groups of the Black-Caribbean and the Bangladeshi populations and both have relatively high rates of morbidity and mortality, as from coronary heart disease.

Hospital services

- London's hospitals are providing above England average levels of service for the older residents of London mainly through a relatively high rate of hospitalisation for those aged less than 75 years from the mixed- and high-status areas.

- The hospitalisation rate for the population of inner-deprived London is, however, exceptionally low in all five-year age-groups of later life. The shortfalls in some age-groups exceed 15 per cent. Over-estimates of the residential population (as above) may account for a proportion of the deficits, but the data recognise FCEs received outside London and the phenomenon is almost certainly real.

- Similarly, occupied hospital bed days *per capita* are at approximately national levels in London as a whole (except among women aged 80+ years for whom they are high), but the older residents of inner-deprived London occupied around one-fifth *fewer* bed days than their equivalents in provincial urban areas.

- Geriatric beds are unevenly provided across London with relatively high provision in scattered DHAs of north London. Shortfalls occur in several inner-deprived areas although this pattern is not consistently reflected in the FCEs for the residents of the different urban zones. Provision in some districts is at twice the rate of others.

- London's low provision of independent and voluntary sector nursing homes, particularly in its inner areas, delays in completing 'care assessments', the high proportion of one-person households, and the prevalence of accommodation with poor access, all make for difficulties in discharge following acute hospital admissions.

- Psychogeriatric services have been developing quickly from a low base over the last decade, but their provision is very uneven across London.

- There is a low rate of FCEs throughout London for 'senile and pre-senile organic psychotic conditions' (roughly equivalent to the most prevalent dementias), in strong contrast to large provincial cities.

- All the large city categories are underprovided with psychogeriatric facilities, with the 60 per cent shortfall in inner London being the greatest deviation.

Community health services

- It is difficult to access comprehensive data on the community health services, and contact data by age is particularly scarce. The available evidence suggests that rates of provision in London are equivalent to national levels but with considerable variability.

- As in the rest of the country, there is considerable diversity in the organisation and profile of the services delivered by community trusts to older people.

- Superficial accounts suggest that the unit costs of community health services are unusually high in London, which is partly explained by the city's high premises and wage costs but is also related to the intensity of patients' needs.

- Some community health care trusts report a very rapid increase in the last few years in the number of older patients requiring intensive services. The male population aged 85 years and over has increased unusually quickly during this period.

- The work of the community health care trusts in London is especially hampered by the scale of London and the large number of acute trusts. They may be most helped by radical innovations in information-handling and exchange.

General practice

- Around a quarter of a million of London's older people consult their general practices every two weeks. The consultation rate is higher than for most adult age-groups but not markedly so among the younger age-group of older men.

- The concerted actions to address long-standing deficiencies of London's general practice services are producing improvements in the sector's premises and support staff. There are however reports that the latter will not continue when special funds cease.

- The proportions of single-handed practices and of sub-standard premises remain high in London, particularly in the inner deprived areas and in the east. There are also fewer practice nurses in London which is probably inimical to carrying out the annual 75 years and over health check.

- The 75 years and over health check is not highly regarded by GPs and many local initiatives for fulfilling the contractual obligations are evident. No widely accepted view about the health benefits or outcomes of the check has become established.

- The impact of the national and London-specific reforms during the 1990s of general practice are unclear. Little evidence of the levels of patient satisfaction is known, but focus group research has revealed a worrying frequency of complaints about both maladministered appointments systems and ageist attitudes.

- As in the rest of the country, patients at the oldest ages receive a high share of GP home visits. There are indications that the frequency of such visits is much below that provided in the rest of the country.

Residential and nursing home places and care

- Local authority residential home places remain relatively plentiful in inner London but under present legislation and funding have no long term future.

- Private sector residential and nursing care is very scarce in inner London and although more plentiful in outer London, its provision is also below national rates. London relies on the relatively abundant provision in the Outer Metropolitan Area and the rest of the South East. Many placements into the independent residential sectors involve a migration towards the periphery of the urban area.

- The main impediments to the provision of independent and voluntary sector residential and nursing home care in London are the high costs of land, property and staff.

Community care

- As in the rest of the country, the implementation of the 1993 community care provisions of the 1990 NHS reforms has been uneven. Fewer 'care assessments' have been completed than are required, and the rate of completion varies considerably among the boroughs.
- There are many local initiatives for joint working between primary care and the community health services, and between these and social services. These demonstrate the need for inter-agency and inter-sector arrangements but rely on goodwill and are vulnerable to changes in personnel.

Synthesis

- The development and effectiveness of health and social services for older people continue to be handicapped by false stereotyping of 'elderly patients' and 'elderly clients'. An accurate, integrated appreciation of the full range of the older population's health care needs is conspicuously rare.
- The dedicated 'care of the elderly' services in both the hospitals and the community have relatively low clinical and scientific prestige. This is probably more damaging in London than in other regions with fewer specialist centres of excellence and less research. Managing chronic conditions is also poorly regarded by many health and social care providers, even though their diagnosis and the determination of treatment courses demands an exceptional breadth of knowledge, assessment skills and attention to the patient's morale and social situation.
- The frequent need among older patients and clients for inter-agency and inter-sectoral care of long duration meets with a systemic weakness. Both the management of older patients' acute episodes of long duration, and multi-agency care to moderately and severely disabled older patients, raise demands for levels of communication and patient-centred care that often are not met. One reason is that no agency or single provider has responsibility for 'holistic' care.
- The planning and regulatory functions of the district health authorities have been weakened and their efforts concentrate upon acute hospitals. Analyses of the state of the public health frequently focus on the variations of greatest amplitude among young adults and do not examine variations in the health status of older people.
- The social service departments' community care plans reveal many problems in implementing a consistent approach to care assessment and care plans for the most dependent people able to live in their own homes. Shortages of finances are usual, but no template for inter-agency co-operation and responsibility has been available and the success of joint working is a function of local circumstances and goodwill.

- Older people with complex needs are falling through the cracks between agencies. Services are fragmented, there are problems with funding, a lack of proper assessment and re-assessment, inequity and inadequate communication.

- The absence of any means to monitor the quality and effectiveness of multi-provider care is a serious impediment to the diagnosis of weaknesses in health and social services for older people and their correction. The present blindness to system performance is a major weakness which is rarely recognised let alone tackled.

- There is a strong case for a fresh start to the implementation of care management. The ambition to provide 'seamless care' should however extend beyond the services for the most frail and dependent older people. The further challenge is to establish effective mechanisms for monitoring, evaluating and managing the complex treatment pathways of acute episodes. There should be effective audit of multi-provider and inter-sectoral care. The powers and duty to correct sub-optimal treatment and care should be clearly defined and allocated to a responsible body.

Chapter 1

Introduction

Summary

- This introductory chapter sets out the objectives and scope of the 'older people' study. This report reviews the socio-demographic and health trends of older people in London and their use of health and social services. It aims to identify the areas of service provision that are functioning well and those which are deficient.

- Where deficiencies are shown, explanations are sought and where possible provided. Often the required information has not come to hand, and hypotheses only are advanced.

- The report necessarily develops a broader view of service provision to the older population than is charged to any NHS sector or providing agency, or would be expected in either local authority social services departments or independent nursing care organisations. Its task is to examine needs and provision 'in the round'. This is achieved by applying at times the 'community health and well-being' perspective of population epidemiology, and at times a 'customer view'.

- Several underlying principles of the synthesis and assessment offered in these pages are also introduced in the chapter. Services for elderly patients and clients are commonly seen to have low prestige. One task for the report is to demonstrate the diversity of this age-group's service requirements and the professional rewards of providing them well.

- Pessimistic stereotypes of the older patient's capacity to recover from sickness and ill-health prevail, partly because lazy generalisations are made about the health and care needs of the age-group. These are often based on the characteristics of the patients and clients of the specialised 'care of the elderly' services, which comprise only a small minority of older people.

- The majority of older people have health problems similar to those of other adults, and the majority of their contacts with the health services are little different from the presentations by the middle-aged. The minority with chronic and multiple disorders, mostly aged at least 75 years, require relatively intensive medical and social care from the primary care, 'care of the elderly', community health, and domiciliary and residential social services and in nursing homes.

- Older people in their 60s and early 70s are much more numerous than those who survive to the oldest ages. In comparison to the middle-aged, they have high needs for the primary and acute health care services, for example for cardiovascular disorders, orthopaedic problems and the cancers. The effective management of inter-sectoral treatment and care is a large element of the age-group's demands for health and social services.

- Given knowledge of the morbidity and social dependency profiles of older people and of some distinctive features of the treatments and care they require, a patient-based assessment of service provision and utilisation is possible.

- The final sections of this chapter develop hypotheses about ways in which the great size and administrative complexity of London could compromise older people's treatment and care. They set an agenda and a range of questions to be tackled later in the report.

1 The task and ambition of this report

No region of the country has more distinctive NHS expenditure and provision than London. No other city has so many social service authorities. No other region has such a diverse ethnic profile, such a distinctive social structure, or is so confounded by movements of people across its boundaries. Like many other European capital cities, London has the greatest concentration in the country of specialist hospitals and units, of teaching and research activity, and of private medical care. Many services to a greater or lesser extent serve a national function, and all serve the entire South East region, within the boundaries of the Thames health regions. The national function is massive in medical research and education but hardly touches general practice. Despite many analyses, it is by no means clear whether or not London's resident population, and particularly its older people, benefit from or are disadvantaged by the distinctive composition and functions of London's health facilities and expenditure. It is to these questions that this study is addressed.

This report overviews the health of the older population of London and their utilisation of health and social care services. Its purpose is to identify those aspects of the current organisation of services and of current practice which are working well and those which are deficient and most in need of reform and improvement. The starting point is the demographic, social and morbidity characteristics of London's older people. In these are found both the bases of *need* for treatment and support, and at least some of the roots of the changing patterns and rising *demand* for services. The second step is to review the administrative fragmentation of older people's services in London. Sectoral divisions characterise services for older people throughout the United Kingdom but are exacerbated in London by its great size and the multiplicity of providing agencies. Given the distinctive service needs of older people, there may be particular implications of the administrative maze. Other features particular to London have been especially deleterious to the provision of community, residential and nursing home facilities and services in London, foremost among which are high prices of land and property, and high wage costs. By examining many types of evidence on the current provision and utilisation of services in London, how they vary across the city, and how the capital compares with the rest of England, several contrasts and some worrying deficiencies are found.

The next step is to understand why the weakest aspects of the present arrangements have come about and persist. Some of the deficiencies are not widely understood. A recurring theme through this report is that there are hardly any mechanisms for monitoring the performance *in the round* of health and social services for older people in London. Because we do not audit the services as a system – for no authority below the Treasury has that responsibility – no one has a clear picture of either the strengths or the weaknesses of the system, nor of recent improvements or deterioration. On the other hand, some specific weaknesses in London's services are widely acknowledged and have attracted special attention. The prominent example is primary health care, which has benefited from massive investments and much commendable innovation during the 1990s. Remarkably, however, there has been no evaluation of the net effects of these efforts from either the providers' or the patients' perspective and, particularly, no assessment of whether or not older people in London themselves find that the primary care services they receive are improving.

It is clear from this report that the statutory health and social services should be supported by high quality 'market research'. Without rigorous evidence about either the performance of the system or the levels of satisfaction in the population, efforts for change and improvement in the health and social services will always be distorted by the caprice of anecdotal opinion. The report also makes suggestions for improvement in specific services and agencies. These are guided by many practical considerations: the malleability of problems, the likely cost of amelioration or a solution, administrative feasibility, and professional acceptability. They also take account of the resolve of the new Government to establish a new London-wide elected authority. Its functions and responsibilities will be debated and defined during 1997. Here clearly is an opportunity to address some of the weaknesses uncovered in this report. Clearly thought-out structures and devices to monitor, inform and stimulate London's health and social services for older people could make a large contribution to supporting the providing agencies and all their staff, and to raising the quality of services received.

2 Guiding precepts

Several general principles underlie this report. Two key assumptions are that the health of any population can be improved, and the efficiency of any health care system raised. It is not necessary to demonstrate that the situation is worse in London than in rest of

England for important and urgent tasks to be present. Comparisons with the rest of England or the United Kingdom are only one basis on which to develop public health and NHS management and policy priorities for promoting the health and well-being of the older population. As soon as we look to the many other countries, say to France, Spain and Switzerland, that have recently achieved much faster improvements than the United Kingdom in old age mortality, it is realised that there is a large task facing the British health and social care services (Caselli, 1994; United Nations Organisation, 1993). There are many weaknesses in Britain's services for older people nationwide and many health problems in the older population that could be tackled more vigorously (Central Health Monitoring Unit, 1992; Grundy, 1992; Medical Research Council, 1994). If Londoners and London's health professionals can lead the way in raising Britain's position in the international health league tables, that will be to the national good.

Another principle is that the health and well-being of older people is neither more nor less important than that of children, those raising families, or those in paid employment. When this proposition is expressed in the abstract, only the most materialist or utilitarian of thinkers objects. In practice, however, in both our everyday lives and in much professional practice these precepts do *not* apply. There is rightly abhorrence of premature deaths, and chronic illness or disability in a young person is generally regarded as tragic. The partly complementary views, that illness is inevitable in old age, or that an incapacity is less of a problem for an older person than for someone in work or with family responsibilities, is however widespread as an unstated assumption if not as an explicit guideline. Such views are pernicious, if only because of the heterogeneity of older people. Physiological reserves, vulnerability to complicating infections, and competence in the instrumental activities of daily living, to name but three considerations in treatment and placement decisions, should always be matters of individual assessment. Generalisations about the characteristics of nonagenarians are too readily formed on the basis of the unrepresentative sample of people who present to medical or social services, and they can easily be extended to a younger group of older people. The safest assumption is that older people are no different from other adults.

A third precept is that there is much confusion about older people's health and social care needs and about the services that are provided for them. This arises from the heterogeneity of the older population, the great range of ages they encompass, and the fact that the services which are explicitly dedicated to them, and are so named, actually provide for specialist needs. There is an analogy here with the comedian's ridicule of stereotypical older drivers. A man or woman in their late 60s driving quite normally does not attract attention and is not dubbed an 'older driver'. Another of the same age driving hesitantly or incompetently causes impatient irritation and fuels demeaning generalisations. Similarly in the health services, a large proportion of older people's contacts with the primary care and hospital services are for conditions and episodes that are no different to those presented by the middle-aged. They are not seen as older people's problems, and are sometimes forgotten in careless statements about the age-group's service needs. The increasing demands for these services are correctly not attributed to the older age-group alone. In these sectors of care, the rising demands from older people are not especially associated with the patients' ages.

Incidence and prevalence of many physical and mental disorders increases with age. The rates rise particularly steeply for chronic and multiple disorders that are partially disabling and which lead to dependency on others for normal domestic lives. The diagnosis and management of multiple disorders is complex and requires special skills, hence the *raison d'être* for 'care of the elderly' services, in hospitals as the 'geriatrics' speciality, and in community health and social services as day centres, domiciliary services and residential and nursing homes for older people. Inevitably there are boundary problems as to which service is appropriate and when. Periodic reviews of local service configurations are laudable signs of active monitoring and appraisal, and careful re-definitions and boundary shifts are in order. For the present argument, however, the particular implication of the existence of specialist 'care of the elderly' services is that they distort the general perception of older people's health care needs and underpin false stereotypes of older people. While health care commissioners and managers would not use 'geriatric' as insensitively as do third-rate entertainers, nearly everyone in the services uses 'the elderly' to mean the most disabled few. This must bedevil assessments and provision of the full range of services to older people. The problems range from nomenclature to funding.[1] The Janus faces of older people's needs and of the service response are yet one more reason for appraisal of the services as a whole from both provider and population perspectives.

3 Are older people and older people's services in London different?

London's older people

It is right to ask whether the special nature of London's health services has a beneficial or harmful effect on London's older people. It will not be argued that London should receive favoured treatment in comparison to the rest of the country. But it is too easy to become complacent about health service provision in London for older people. On the most superficial aggregate indicators, such as the standard mortality ratios or self-reported measures of health, London's older population seems healthier than in the rest of the country. Average incomes, educational levels and occupational status in the general

---

1 The preferred usage in the London health services world in 1997 has replaced 'geriatric medicine' (as appears in statistical returns) with 'care of the elderly'. The latter term will generally be used in this report. It is of interest, however, that in social policy circles the term 'the elderly' is rapidly being replaced by 'older people'.

population are higher in London than in other parts of the country, and much higher than in the large provincial cities. During most years of the current older population's lives, unemployment has been lower in London than elsewhere. London has not had the very poor public health conditions found in the former coal mining and heavy industrial areas of the country. The most common general view is that London's population, including its older members, is relatively advantaged. But the general prosperity of London conceals districts of the most intense deprivation in the country (Department of the Environment, 1995). These are concentrated in an inner ring of boroughs and are at their most intense in Tower Hamlets, Hackney and Lambeth.

There are other special features. London's population has unusually high social and residential mobility. Migration arrivals and departures are very high, not only because of the high turnover of young people. One distinctive feature of the capital is the large exodus of people approaching or at retirement age. There is an over-representation of the more prosperous among those who leave, which must reduce the average incomes of those who remain. The relative health and social status of London's resident older population is confounded by these migrations and is certainly not uniformly high. The report examines the effect of this selective emigration on the social and health characteristics of London's resident older people.

Two other special factors in London's population need to be considered in the light of its particular configuration of services. These arise from the city's great size and the migration and population mobility that has been described. A high proportion of London's older people live alone and it has been argued for decades that localised kin networks are less common in the capital than elsewhere (Eversley, 1982). The reasoning is that a low fraction of Londoners are native, and that the children of a high proportion have moved to distant suburbs and beyond. Although there is little to document this in standard statistical sources, some survey evidence will be reviewed. The implication is that dependent older people in London are not supported by their families or informal carers to the same extent as in more stable areas of the country. London certainly has relatively little residential and nursing home provision for older people. If informal care is also less available than elsewhere, the consequence would be high demands upon the community health, domiciliary social and primary care services. Community and social services have a lower profile with the general public, the media and politicians, and less professional prestige than the hospital services. This is reflected in London as elsewhere by the paucity and poor quality of the available statistics for these sectors. This report later demonstrates considerable variability in the provision of certain of these services, and presents firm evidence that older people in some parts of London are particularly poorly served.

London's attraction for migrants has also given it the most cosmopolitan and ethnically diverse population of the country. The phasing of the large immigration flows from the Caribbean, the Indian sub-continent and East Africa has been such that the next few decades will see rapid increases in the number of older people in the minority ethnic groups. The relatively low job skills and incomes of large sections of these populations have given them a weak position in London's housing markets which, combined with real and perceived discrimination, has resulted in low rates of dispersal and the persistence of concentrated clusters of minority ethnic people in the city. The net result is that there will be special demands on providers in many parts of London, particularly its inner districts, and especially on the primary, community and social services.

The appropriateness of service organisation for the older population

It is also well-known that expenditure on hospital services is higher *per capita* in London than in the rest of the country, and that inner London is generously provided with large, prestigious teaching hospitals. Surely, some would say, this must be to the advantage of London's older-age-groups as well as others. But as a recent London Commission study has confirmed, the rate of hospitalisation for the resident population of inner London is lower than the comparable rates in provincial inner cities (Boyle and Hamblin, 1997). The extent of this 'under-provision' for London's older residents is examined in detail. For some specialties and procedures, the situation for older people is markedly more unfavourable than for those of working age.

There are also good reasons for suspecting that the administrative and organisational fragmentation of health and social services for older people in London reduces the volume and quality of the services they receive. The management of many serious and chronic disorders often requires referral between providers. In London so many patient referrals cross health authority and local authority boundaries that poor communication increases the problems of collaboration among sectors, providing agencies and individual practitioners. These problems are most evident in the responses to acute episodes and hospital discharge, and in the co-ordination of primary care and community health and personal social service support for those with chronic and disabling conditions. Do the internal communication systems work well? Are London's hospitals and many excellent units efficiently used by patients? Does the scale of London and the plethora of agencies and specialist facilities counteract the advantages of living alongside the nation's largest medical centre of excellence? And if these structural weaknesses do indeed exist, are the negative consequences most evident among older patients and clients? Older people occasionally experience discrimination (Dudley and Burns, 1992; Royal College of Physicians, 1995), and many physicians have remarked that they are the group of patients with the least expectations and most deference (Royal Colleges of Physicians, 1994; Swift, 1989).

If we turn our attention to other sectors of health and social care provision for older people, a common feature is that the 1990s have seen major national policy, institutional and professional changes. Many well-informed people and certainly the general public have been bewildered by the volume and intricacy of the changes. In many cases not even superficial generalisations have formed about their net effect. For example, little is known about the impact on patients of the rationalisation of A&E services or of the changes in London's primary care. Most of all, the net effects of the community care provisions of the 1990 NHS Act are unclear, and it does not seem likely that policy and practice in this area will quickly stabilise.

Rather, the tendency is for further dimensions of uncertainty to be added. Acute trusts struggle to resolve the conflicts between their own productivity, the need of some of the frailest older patients for long-term care and supported accommodation, and the absence of suitable vacancies or the funds to pay for them. The role of general practice consortia in the locality-purchasing of acute services is likely to strengthen, and some boundaries between primary care, community health and social services may change. Social services departments have found it difficult to reduce their role as direct providers of residential and domiciliary care as quickly as the previous Government would have liked, but have reduced funds with which to sustain these inherited roles. Private residential and nursing care homes may soon emerge from a period of low growth and rationalisation, stimulated by a recovering housing market that encourages the conversion of housing assets into disposable income. They will continue however to be most affected by frequent revisions to the regulations setting entitlements to DSS fees support. Over and above all these sources of instability, the new Government may introduce further substantial changes in primary care, the personal social services and in the financing of new NHS buildings, including the much heralded local community health facilities. Given this maelstrom of change, which arguably has affected older people more than any other patient (or client) group, and which in London will at least have special dimensions, broad-based evaluations of the impact on patients of the rapidly changing system of care are needed.

4 Sources of data and structure of the report

Many people have contributed to the collection of information, the analyses and the arguments which are brought together in this report. Several thematic information papers were commissioned for the study and have been listed. Other London Commission studies have provided invaluable data, notably *London's Mental Health* (Johnson *et al.*, 1997). The research staff of the London Commission have supplied many new analyses of the NHS utilisation data, and their recent report on *The Health Economy of London* has been extensively used (Boyle and Hamblin, 1997). The project's support group have given generously of their time.

Several sources of data and approaches to their analysis and presentation are common to other reports of the London Commission and particularly to the just-mentioned *Health Economy of London.* Often reference is made to variations across London. These sometimes employ National Health Service purchasing agency areas and sometimes the boroughs of London, with on occasion references to the 16 district health authorities (as of 1996) and the 33 London boroughs (as of 1986 and including the City of London with only some 4,000 residents).[2] There are also occasional references to five geographical sectors: North West, North Central, East, South East and South London. The most frequent comparisons are among a threefold division of socio-economic areas: inner-deprived, mixed-status and high-status for both London and non-London (or the rest of England). The definitions of these areas were set out as an appendix to *The Health Economy of London* and are reproduced in this volume as Appendix 1.

While the socio-economic divisions are immensely valuable in permitting comparisons with the equivalent areas of England's provincial cities and urban areas, as for any territorial classification built up from relatively large geographical units, one must be aware of their idiosyncrasies and limitations. To mention just three oddities: both the City of Westminster and the Borough of Tower Hamlets are classified as inner-deprived; the Borough of Harrow is classified as mixed-status; while the Borough of Bromley is high status yet they have innumerable similarities; and among the non-London high-status health authorities are a great mix of areas, from Huntingdon to Nottingham and Stockport.

The chapters of this report focus successively on the social and health characteristics of London's older people, pertinent distinctive features of London's health and social services, and current profiles of contact and utilisation. That sequence might be characterised as 'need', 'framework' and 'provision'. Chapter 5 brings together the issues identified earlier and offers, from the perspectives and concerns of older people, both an enumeration and some evaluation of the greatest deficiencies of the capital's statutory health and social services system. The final chapter is an exposition of possible action and desirable futures. The report uncovers many causes for concern, not all of which are special to London. One firm conclusion is that older people's needs and problems receive much less attention than their prominence as customers of the health and social services deserves.

---

2. It should be noted that most of the data was compiled when four NHS Regions – NE, NW, SW and SE Thames – quartered Greater London and spread far beyond. The four were rationalised to the North Thames and South Thames Regions in 1996. They are of little value as statistical units for studies of London.

Chapter 2

London's older people

Summary

- A relatively low share of London's population is aged 60 years and over. The shortfall is mainly of people aged 65–74 years, and the average age of London's older people is higher than in England.

- The older population of London is set to fall until around 2005.

- London has the highest proportion of minority ethnic older people of any region of the country, and the number will increase rapidly over the next decade, led by Black-Caribbean men and women.

- Men are in the majority among those in their 50s and 60s in the Black-Caribbean and Bangladeshi minority ethnic groups. These groups include many with low incomes, have high age-specific mortality and are concentrated in the most deprived areas of inner London (and the country).

- Among all British cities and regions, London has the highest rates of out-migration among late middle-aged and older people. Among those in their 60s the exodus is concentrated in owner-occupiers and above-average income groups. The consequence is to lower the socio-economic profile of London's older people in comparison to the working-aged. The exodus is also found among people at the highest ages, among whom a high proportion move to live near or with a relative or carer or into institutions.

- Among British metropolitan areas, some outer London boroughs have very high rates of in-migration of people aged 75 years and over. A combination of high representations of the higher income groups and clusters of residential and nursing homes are responsible. The inflows are lower than in specialised retirement towns, as on the south coast.

- Broadly the epidemiology of older people in London is similar to that elsewhere in the United Kingdom. The majority of those in their 60s and 70s are without disability. Levels of disability increase with age but remain a minority characteristic until the 80s. The incidence of acute clinical episodes increases with age from late middle-age, and rises sharply in the five years before death.

- Age-specific mortality rates are generally more favourable in London than in the rest of the country. Remarkably, this advantage appears to extend to inner-deprived areas, although inaccurate estimates of the 'usually resident' population, particularly for the oldest ages and for women, may distort the figures.

> • The majority of older people have health problems similar to those of other adults, and the majority of their contacts with the health services differ little from the presentations by the middle-aged. The minority with chronic and multiple disorders, mostly aged at least 75 years, require relatively intensive medical and social care from the primary care, 'care of the elderly', community health, and domiciliary and residential social services and in nursing homes.

1 The diversity of ages among London's older people

This chapter sets out the main facts about London's older population and its health, disability and dependency profiles. The range of topics to be covered is large, partly because older people are themselves immensely diverse. The first of several reasons for the diversity is the great range of ages among older people. The youngest female pensioners in their early 60s are more than 50 years younger than the oldest women alive. Age differences denote another source of heterogeneity, the considerable differentials in the living, working and health conditions that the youngest and eldest have experienced.

In mid-1995, there were around 117,000 Londoners aged 85 years and over. Only a minority would have received secondary school education. Many would have begun their working lives during or before the First World War. While nearly every other woman would have had some adolescent experience as a domestic servant, few would have worked for two decades after the birth of their first child. Most men would have been in manual occupations. By contrast, none of the 288,000 Londoners aged 60–64 years in 1995 would have begun normal paid work until after the Second World War, only a minority of men would have had manual occupations, and with smaller families, many more women would have worked.

These social changes, and particularly the accompanying improvements in the standard of living, housing conditions, diet and access to health care, have produced great changes in the experience of illness of the older population. In 1901–5, around the time when the oldest group were born, the infant mortality rate in England and Wales was 138 per 1,000, but by the birth years of today's youngest pensioners, 1931–35, it had halved to 62 per 1,000 (OPCS, 1989). As the role of environmental factors in differential longevity is reduced, the associations between the conditions of an individual's gestation, birth and first year of life and their adult vulnerability to a range of diseases are of increasing significance (Barker 1992, 1994; Evans, 1994). The immense improvements in survival are also shown by standardised mortality ratios (SMR) which compare the prevailing schedule of age-specific death rates with those of 1990 (=100). In 1901–5 the SMR was 366, and in 1931–35 it was 197. The contrasts have continued into old age. Today's 86 year old attained 60 years in 1971 when the death rate at ages 55–64 years was 14.9 per 1,000. Recent decades have seen unprecedented decreases in mortality at the older ages, and just 21 years later, in 1992, the 55–64 years' death rate had declined by 29 per cent to 10.6 per 1,000 (OPCS, 1994).

Through this century, the material and health standards of the British population have clearly improved immensely, and there is little doubt that these have contributed to a decrease in late-age mortality and improved age-specific health among older people, at least in the younger age-groups (Grundy, 1992a). There are, of course, contrary indicators, of which the most important by far has been the substantial increase in cigarette smoking among those born after the 1920s, the harmful consequences of which will continue to increase in the older population for perhaps three decades. After 2020, some benefits of the reduction in tobacco consumption, at least among males, should begin to influence patterns of disease in older people.

Service providers are less aware of the long-term trend towards the improved health of older people than of their rising demand for treatments and care. The apparent paradox is explained by three things. Firstly, the number of older people in the country has increased. Secondly, advances in medicine have increased life expectancy after diagnosis of many of the more common diseases of old age, not least the cancers and cardiovascular disorders, but the patients remain under care. This trend has prompted a vigorous debate on both sides of the Atlantic as to whether it is 'healthy and active life expectancy' or 'disabled life expectancy' that is most increasing. As will be examined further, the latest evidence is that age-specific disability levels are steady in Great Britain (and falling in the United States). Thirdly, there have been strongly rising health and social care expectations in all age-groups. There is rising demand for services, from older people as well as others, but the main reason is not increased numbers but increased 'utilisation'.

Older people display all levels of health and functioning. Two-thirds of Londoners aged 60 years and over did not report a limiting long-standing illness to the 1994 General Household Survey. The London Research Centre (LRC) estimates that in 1996 just over half of Londoners aged 65 years had no disability, just over a fifth only low disability and the rest moderate or high disability (the details are examined later). The implication of this variability is that older people have diverse health and social care needs. It is widely understood that the incidence and prevalence of many of the common disabling conditions increases geometrically with age in later life, and that multiple and chronic disorders are especially common at the most advanced ages. Less widely appreciated is that at any one time the proportion of older people in the more severe categories of disability is very low. The LRC estimated that only 6 per cent of the population aged 65 years and over in 1996 were in the most severe disability categories (OPCS Disability

Survey categories 9 and 10). Among those aged 85 years and over, however, one-fifth were so disabled.

Another window on the high frequency but 'normality' of older people's health conditions is the low utilisation of 'care of the elderly' services by the younger age-groups – to a large extent by design, for hospital practice has often routed those aged less than 75 years through the 'acute' specialty units (Hall, 1988). In 1994–95, people in their 60s made up 45 per cent of London's population aged 60 years and over. The age-group accounted for 35 per cent of all finished consultant episodes (FCE) in London's hospitals, but only 1.4 per cent of these FCEs were provided by the geriatric medicine specialty. Communal and especially nursing homes also serve principally octogenarians and nonagenarians who are frail, sick and socially isolated. Only 6.3 per cent of inner London's 85 years olds and over, and 9.3 per cent in outer London were residents of nursing homes in 1991, much lower than the 15.3 per cent in Great Britain. Another 5.9 and 5.3 per cent respectively were in other types of communal establishments. But these very old residents of institutions made up only 1.8 per cent of London's pensionable age population. The majority of older people do not have the characteristics of those who receive the dedicated 'care of the elderly' and 'older people' services.

2 The age structure and distribution of London's older population

London's population has a high share in the working ages and a complementarily low share of older people. If the English age structure applied to London, it would have had an additional 177,000 people aged 60 years and over. Examination of the details of London's age structure shows however that the deficit of older people is concentrated among those aged 65–74 years (Table 2.1). In 1995 there were an estimated 87,400 women aged 85 years and over in London and they formed 2.4 per cent of the female population. In England as a whole, there were 581,400 women of this age, 2.7 per cent of the all-age population. In other words, the shortfall in this age-group was just 10,000 or 10 per cent. The deficit among males aged 85 and over was also low, at 7,700 or 14 per cent. In comparison with the rest of England, London in 1992 had a larger share of its older male population in the late working ages (60–64 years), and it had a larger share of its older men and women aged 75 years and over. Put another way, although the population of London has a relatively low share aged 60 years and over, within that age-group the average ages of men and of women aged 65 or over are higher than in the rest of England.

The age structure of London's older population is of practical importance for many of the health and social services. General practitioners are expected to provide an annual health check to their patients aged 75 years and over. They and their practice staff make many more home visits to patients at these advanced ages than to younger older people.

Table 2.1 The age structure of London's older population, 1995

Age group	Greater London, Males				Greater London, Females				Rest of England	
	Pop'tn 000s	% 60+	Ratio to rest	% 0+	Pop'tn 000s	% 60+	Ratio to rest	% 0+	m % 60+	fm % 60+
60-64	143.4	27.5	1.04	4.2	145.0	20.4	1.00	4.1	26.3	20.4
65-69	124.2	23.8	0.98	3.6	139.2	19.6	0.96	3.9	24.4	20.4
70-74	105.9	20.3	0.95	3.1	136.1	19.2	0.95	3.8	21.4	20.1
75-79	70.1	13.4	0.98	2.0	107.9	15.2	1.00	3.0	13.7	15.2
80-84	48.6	9.3	1.04	1.4	93.5	13.2	1.06	2.6	9.0	12.5
85+	29.3	5.6	1.07	0.9	87.4	12.3	1.08	2.4	5.3	11.5
60+	521.4	100		15.2	709.2	100		19.8	3,754	5,056
0+	3,432			100	3,575			100	20,576	21,320

The dedicated 'care of the elderly' services as well as residential and nursing home care are largely aimed at the same advanced old age-groups. It is therefore important that the relatively low share of older people by comparison with the country is not allowed to hide the fact that London has a larger number of very old people than might be expected.

The 1991 Great Britain census adopted a classification of local authority districts by 11 settlement-landscape types devised by John Craig of OPCS. They range from two divisions of both London (inner and outer) and the metropolitan counties (cores and rings) to remote rural areas.[1] Most reported total and elderly age structures very close to the national pattern. Among the large-city classes, inner London had the most distinctive age structure, with a 17 per cent under-representation of pensioners that balanced its high over-representation of very young adults (aged 15–29 years) and young children (<5 years). Young pensioners were most under-represented (Warnes, 1991).

The London Commission studies are mainly concerned with Greater London, but it should be noted that the functional metropolitan area extends far beyond the territory of the London boroughs. The rate of decentralisation or suburbanisation has tended to accelerate through this century: the most recent surge was during the housing boom of the 1980s. One result has been that over the last 20 years, the age structure of inner London has changed relatively rapidly in comparison with the rest of England and Wales. The change has much to do with the expansion of the metropolis and the internal rearrangement of its people. The long-recognised statistical unit of the London Metropolitan Area (LMA) comprises the former Greater London County (GLC), incorporating inner and outer London, and the surrounding Outer Metropolitan Area (OMA). It extends approximately 40 miles (65 km) from the centre. Its overall population decreased from 12.6 million in 1971 to 11.8 million in 1991, but throughout this period

---

1. The Metropolitan Counties were disbanded as administrative authorities in 1986, but the constituent Metropolitan Districts continue.

Table 2.2 The distribution of the pensionable population in the London metropolis, 1971-1991

Zone	Number (000s)			Share of total (%)			Location quotients		
	1971	1981	1991	1971	1981	1991	1971	1981	1991
Inner London	375	335	273	16.1	17.5	15.4	1.05	1.04	0.91
Outer London	849	866	801	16.5	18.0	17.3	1.07	1.07	1.03
Outer Metro. Area	720	836	922	14.0	15.5	16.9	0.91	0.92	1.00
London Metro. Area	1,944	2,036	1,996	15.4	16.8	16.9	1.00	1.00	1.00

Note: The pensionable population includes males aged 65 years and over and females aged 60 years and over.

the population of pensionable age stood around 2 million: it increased by nearly 5 per cent during the 1970s and fell by nearly the same amount during the 1980s (Table 2.2).

Greater London changed from 1971 to 1991 from having a relatively old population to become the English metropolitan area with the lowest pensionable share. In 1971, a long established pattern was found of a relatively old population in inner London and a relatively young periphery, but by 1991 the distribution had changed to a young core, a relatively old middle-ring, and an outer ring with the national share of older people. In 1971, inner London had a 5 per cent excess of pensioners in relation to the LMA and the outer ring had a 9 per cent deficit. By 1991 inner London had acquired the 9 per cent deficit, outer London had an *over*-representation of people aged 75 years and over but the next ring, the OMA, had an *under*-representation of this age-group. Further from the centre still, the rest of the South East had a substantial over-representation of all age-groups above 60 years.

As the distribution has changed by rings, so there have been marked shifts within the London Metropolitan Area. There was a contiguous belt of districts with high elderly shares in the south-west sector of both the GLC and the Home Counties. Within Greater London, the distribution was complex although, apart from the Boroughs of Camden and the City of Westminster, only outer boroughs were found in the highest quintile of the values of all GB local authorities (>19.1 per cent). On the other hand, aside from the City of London, only Havering on the north-eastern periphery had a pensionable share in the lowest two quintiles (Warnes, 1987).

Figure 2.1 maps the distributions of older population shares by local authorities in 1971 and 1991. In 1971, as in 1981, high elderly shares were found almost exclusively in inner London and the high-status south west sector. There were relatively few older people in the OMA, except for high shares in Southend and Tunbridge Wells. By 1991, the central concentration of the older population had lessened and the locations of relative concentrations had changed. No inner London borough had an older share in the highest quartile, i.e. the formerly high concentrations of older people in Kensington & Chelsea and Westminster had been much reduced. Although high shares of older people continued to extend from the London Boroughs of Richmond and Kingston-upon-Thames south west into Surrey and West Sussex, the distinctiveness of this sector had reduced. Other outer London boroughs, such as Bromley, Barnet and Havering, had joined the highest quartile, and a ring of districts with high over-representations had formed just beyond the boundary of the former Greater London County.

The implications of these rapid distributional changes for London's health and social services are twofold. One general effect of the high rate of deconcentration is to increase the distinctiveness of inner London's age structure. The central and inner areas are becoming more dedicated to commerce, administration, training, tourism and cultural organisations, and their attractiveness and affordability for family and retirement residence is decreasing. Inner London's population is increasingly dominated by very young adults, recent immigrants and the lowest income groups. Although high income areas persist in inner west and north west London, and during the 1980s gentrified areas expanded in Lambeth, Wandsworth, Islington and Docklands (and may do so again), they are populated by households who increasingly possess second homes elsewhere. The retention of this population when retired is low, and among the oldest residents of inner London, low income groups are more prevalent than London's social structure would suggest. The pace of deconcentration and re-distribution is unlikely to abate, and it can be predicted confidently that inner London's older population will see a rapidly rising share from the minority ethnic groups.

The other broad implication is that there is a progressively smaller residential population of older people in London for its hospitals to serve. Adjustments to the geography of London's health services in line with the changing distribution of its people have been late and little. As Chapter 4 will show, this has not produced benefits for inner London's older people, for their hospitalisation rates are distinctly low. Given the general case for reductions in inner London's hospital provision, it will be increasingly difficult to gain approval for investments or changes in policy that correct the under-provision to inner London's residents.

3 Projections of the older population

From the perspective of London's health and social service agencies, the evolution of the demography of its older population is most important in terms of the absolute number of people to be served, and the size of the projected changes over the short and medium terms. The LRC has made detailed age-group projections for London for the period 1991–2011. The total number of people of pensionable age (60/65 years and over) is 'likely to fall from 1,126,000 in 1991 to 992,000 in 2006, before recovering slightly to

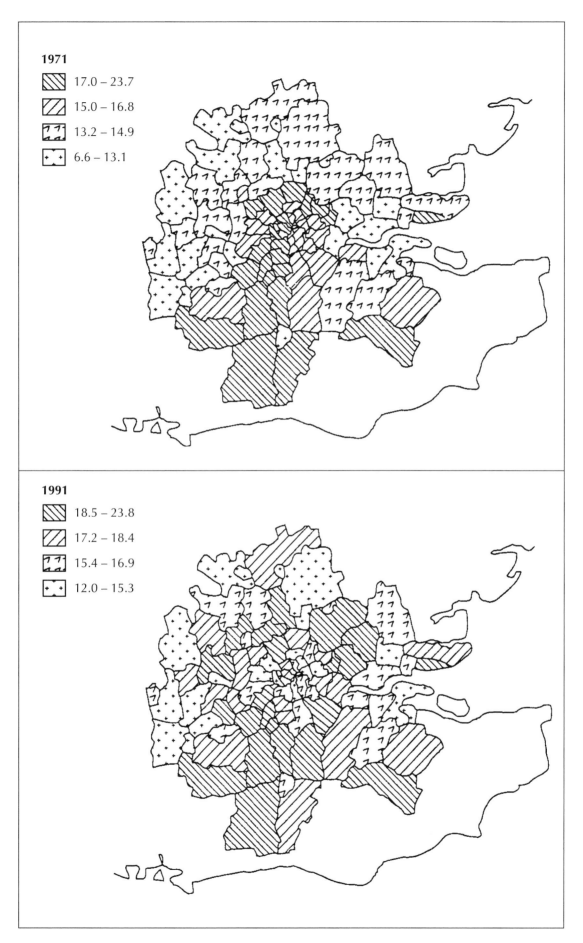

Figure 2.1 The distribution of the pensionable population in the local authority areas of the London Metropolitan Area (percentages of the total population)

1,003,000 in 2011. The net migration loss of older residents is partly responsible for this decline, but the main reason is the actual age structure of London's residents in 1991 and the ageing of each cohort'. Similarly, the population aged 65 years and over is likely to decrease from 970,000 in 1991 to 828,000 in 2011, while the number aged 85 years and over is likely to increase during the 1990s from 101,000 to 119,000, but to fall during the first decade of the next century by 5,000.

The projected absolute changes in the Greater London population for successive five-year periods and by sex and age-group are presented in Table 2.3. The early-1990s saw atypically large increases among those aged 85 years and over of 5,000 men (+24 per cent) and 8,000 women (+10.5 per cent). Several special factors were responsible. Although there were fewer births in Great Britain during 1906–16 than in the preceding ten years, the younger cohort did not suffer large losses of men during the First World War (hence the substantial sex differential in the increase). Secondly, during the 1920s and 1930s, London's economy was buoyant and there was substantial net migration into London (Thomas, 1962).

The projected rate of increase of the 85 years and over population moderates during the later 1990s and becomes negative for females and for the aggregate population during

Table 2.3 Projections of the older population of London, 1996–2011

	65–74 years		75–84 years		85 years and over		65 years and over	
	Number (000s)	^% over 5 yrs before	Number (000s)	^% over 5 yrs before	Number (000s)	^% over 5 yrs before	Number (000s)	^% over 5 yrs before
Males								
1991	232		127		24		382	
1996	223	-3.7	119	-6.3	29	23.9	371	-2.9
2001	211	-5.5	117	-1.6	32	8.4	359	-3.2
2006	204	-3.4	114	-2.7	32	0.1	349	-2.9
2011	205	0.6	109	-3.8	33	3.6	347	-0.6
Females								
1991	287		223		78		589	
1996	266	-7.5	200	-10.3	86	10.5	551	-6.2
2001	242	-9.1	185	-7.4	88	2.2	516	-6.7
2006	233	-3.6	173	-6.9	83	-5.1	490	-5.0
2011	241	3.5	159	-8.0	81	-2.5	481	-1.6
Males and females								
1991	519		350		101		970	
1996	489	-5.8	319	-8.9	115	13.6	922	-4.9
2001	452	-7.4	302	-5.2	119	3.8	874	-5.3
2006	436	-3.5	286	-5.2	115	-3.7	837	-4.1
2011	446	2.2	268	-6.3	114	-0.8	828	-1.1

Source: LRC, 1995 Round of Projections 1

Note: ^% - percentage change over five years before

2001–6. An increase of 3.6 per cent in the male population aged 85 years and over is expected during 2006–11, reflecting the post-First World War 'baby boom' but also owing something to the improvements in survival during later life that have been achieved over the last quarter century. The next strong surge in the very old population of the country will be in the 2030s, when the high post-Second World War birth cohorts reach 85 years. But for London no projection so far ahead is of value, because so much will depend upon in- and out-migration of that cohort (and all others) over the intervening period.

The unusual situation of London's older population projections is shown in Table 2.4, which compares the projections for the three largest provincial metropolitan areas and the southern regions of England. Only the West Midlands conurbation will experience a decrease of young older people similar to that of London, and all non-London areas are forecast to have increases of those aged 75 years and over. The anticipated increase of this age-group over just eight years is one-sixth or more in East Anglia, the South West and the 'ring' around the conurbation in the West Midlands.

The LRC has also produced population projections for the individual health authorities. It should be emphasised that at this scale, migration transfers are particularly susceptible to changed economic growth and urban re-development. The greatest anticipated losses of older people during the later 1990s are from Kingston & Richmond, Merton, Sutton & Wandsworth, and Barnet, probably reflecting their high rate of out-migration of the retirement-age-groups (Table 2.5). The lowest anticipated losses are from Croydon, Bexley & Greenwich, Enfield & Haringey and Brent & Harrow, which have large blue collar populations and substantial tracts of local authority housing. During the first half of the following decade, 2000–04, the pensionable population of London is expected to fall by 2.6 per cent, with the variation among HAs much as before. During 2005–09, however, the London pensionable population is anticipated to increase by 1.1 per cent,

Table 2.4 Projected population change, two age-groups of older people, 1993–2001

Sub-division	Change (%) 60-74	75+	Region	Change (%) 60-74	75+
Inner London	–8.9	–0.5	Greater Manchester M.C.	–6.6	6.6
Outer London	–7.4	0.1	Merseyside M.C.	–6.2	7.3
Greater London	–7.9	–0.1	Remainder of the N.W.	–1.8	12.6
Remainder of the S.E.	–0.6	12.5	**North West Region**	–4.7	9.1
South East Region	–3.2	8.0			
West Midlands M.C.	–8.5	11.9	**East Anglia**	–2.5	18.9
Remainder of the W. Midlands	–0.7	17.4			
West Midlands Region	–4.6	14.7	**South West**	–4.2	16.9

Source: OPCS 1993b. *National Population Projections, 1991 based.* HMSO: London
Note: M.C. Metropolitan County

Table 2.5 Projections of the pensionable age population, London health authorities, 1996–2011

Health Authority	Zone	1996 000s	2001 000s	2001 ^%	2006 000s	2006 ^%	2011 000s	2011 ^%
East London & The City	1	78	75	–3.6	73	–3.2	72	–0.8
Camden & Islington	1	51	49	–5.5	47	–2.5	49	+2.5
Kensington, Chelsea & Westminster	1	49	47	–3.8	46	–1.0	48	+3.0
Lambeth, Southwark & Lewisham	1	104	98	–5.4	93	–5.1	92	–1.4
Redbridge & Waltham Forest	2	71	68	–4.8	66	–2.0	67	+1.8
Merton, Sutton & Wandsworth	2	94	87	–7.0	84	–4.0	84	+0.7
Enfield & Haringey	2	71	69	–2.8	68	–1.0	69	+1.8
Brent & Harrow	2	67	65	–2.4	65	–1.2	65	+0.8
Ealing, Hammersmith & Hounslow	2	91	88	–3.8	86	–2.2	87	+1.1
Kingston & Richmond	3	51	47	–7.4	46	–3.1	47	+2.8
Croydon	3	50	49	–1.3	49	–0.3	50	+3.1
Bexley & Greenwich	3	71	69	–3.4	68	–1.3	70	+2.2
Bromley	3	56	54	–3.8	53	–1.9	54	+1.5
Barking & Havering	3	73	70	–4.1	68	–3.5	68	+0.1
Barnet	3	51	47	–7.7	45	–4.1	45	+1.0
Hillingdon	3	38	37	–4.1	36	–2.9	36	+0.4
Inner-deprived	Σ1	282	269	–4.6	260	–3.4	260	+0.3
Mixed-status	Σ2	321	306	–4.7	300	–1.2	304	+1.3
High-status	Σ3	463	443	–4.3	432	–2.5	438	+1.4
Greater London		1066	1018	–4.5	992	–2.6	1003	+1.1

Source: LRC, 1995 Round of Projections 1

Note: ^% - percentage change over five years before

with the highest increases (3.0+ per cent) in Kensington, Chelsea and Westminster, and Croydon. The gains in inner London will be much less than in outer London. Decreases are projected to continue in East London & the City and in Lambeth, Southwark and Lewisham.

4 Migration and the turnover of London's older population

The characteristics of older people as of other age-groups can change rapidly in London for two reasons. A stark consequence of the death rate of 47 per 1,000 at 60 years and over is that almost a half of the older population is replaced in a decade. A second cause is the high migration rate. Over at least the last 20 years, as many as one quarter of those passing through retirement have left Greater London (Cribier and Kych, 1993; Stuart, 1987; Warnes, 1994). It is therefore important to examine the cohort in their 50s on the threshold of the eligible ages, and to consider the differential propensities to leave of various social and ethnic groups. The highest departure rates from London among young older people (60–74 years) are from a contiguous belt of districts in the south west sector. Male rates of out-migration from this area approach 5 per cent each year. If continued over seven successive years (of distributed retirements), there would be a gross out-migration of 20.2 per cent. The outer metropolitan counties of Surrey, Berkshire, Hertfordshire and Buckinghamshire have comparable rates of out-migration: the extensive reach of the area around London which exports a high proportion of its retiring age-group deserves wider notice. Much the same areas have relatively high out-migration rates of people aged 75 and over. The south east and north east sectors participate least in this dispersion.

No London or outer metropolitan district has above-national rates of in-migration of young older people but nor do any have exceptionally low rates (as found widely among provincial inner cities). On the other hand, London boroughs produce some of the highest rates of in-migration of people of 75 years and over among local authorities in Great Britain. Kensington & Chelsea, Richmond, Kingston, Croydon and Bromley are strong attractors. Bromley was the only FPC/FHSA district in England during the late 1970s and the 1980s to have very high rates (i.e. 2+ standard deviations above the local authority mean) of out-migration of people of retirement age *and* similarly high rates of female 75 years and over in-migration.

A peculiarity of London's population geography is that there is an unusually strong migration of people in the oldest working ages (55–64 years) into the central Boroughs of Westminster and Kensington & Chelsea. They had the highest rates of in-migration among the local authorities of the South East Region in 1990–1, with respective rates 2.8 and 2.4 standard deviations above the mean (on transformed distributions) (Warnes and Ford, 1995). Westminster combined this distinction with the second lowest rate of in-migration in the South East Region of people aged 85 years and over (after Hammersmith). This flow into central London by those in late working-age corroborates a finding from NHS patient re-registration data. Property prices and rents in these boroughs will ensure that the flow has an over-representation of higher income groups: there probably are many senior managers and professionals among the migrants. Many will have residences elsewhere, and most will leave when their organisational responsibilities cease. This detail is consistent with the relatively large presence within London's over 60 population of males aged 60–64 years (Table 2.1), and it prompts the realisation that the high social status of London's resident senior employed age-groups probably spills over to the youngest statutory retirement ages and will, if only marginally, disguise the prevalence of disadvantage among the oldest age-groups.

A recent integrated analysis of 1991 census migration data and the NHS patient re-registration data by Stillwell *et al.* (1996) has provided more details of the capital's exceptional migration exchanges. The Greater London migration profile 'shows dramatic swings from one age cluster to the next' and very low ratios of in- to out-migration in the early retirement years (Table 2.6). The authors clustered all five-year age-groups into five classes distinguished by their spatial patterns of migration. As can be seen in Panel B of the table, among those aged 60–74 years, for every five people who left Greater

Table 2.6 Migration losses and gains: London, other metropolitan areas and the rest of England by age group, 1990-91

Area	Age groups (years) and migration 'life-stage' types					
	Family 1-15, 30-59	Leavers 16-19	Joiners 20-29	Retirement 60-74	Old age 75+	Total 0+
A. Net migration						
Greater London	−40,303	2,158	−512	−8,037	−3,811	−50,505
% of out-migrants	79.8	−4.2	1.0	15.9	7.5	100
Other metropolitan	−12,450	−1,360	−8,782	−2,975	−2,022	−27,589
% of out-migrants	45.1	4.9	31.8	10.8	7.3	100
B. Ratios of in-migration to out-migration rates						
Greater London	0.43	1.46	0.99	0.19	0.26	
Rest of South	1.17	1.05	1.07	1.37	1.37	
Other metropolitan	0.85	0.88	0.88	0.65	0.62	
Rest of England	1.21	0.90	1.02	1.38	1.31	

Source: Stilwell, Rees and Duke-Williams, 1996, Table 16.6

London, only one entered. This compares with a balance of three leavers to two entrants in the provincial metropolitan areas of England. The London imbalance was slightly less among those aged 75 years and over: for every four who departed, one moved in. The exodus of older people made up 23 per cent of all out-migrants from London. (One should note that the time series of DHA/FHSA patient re-registration data demonstrates that the census year 1990–91 witnessed exceptionally low migration rates in England, which all commentators associate with the collapse of the housing market at that time.)

The social selectivity of out-migrants from London has been repeatedly demonstrated from census and survey sources. The clearest discriminator is that the great majority of leavers are owner-occupiers. Very few local authority tenants are able to move away upon retirement. Married couples are much over-represented in the retirement-age exodus, while at the oldest ages, widows and widowers have a high propensity to move, but generally over short distances. Many other details are known, but it remains difficult to assess the net effect of the out-migration on the characteristics of the London population that remains. One example of the difficulty is the equivocal role of poor health in prompting relocation. Surveys of retired migrants in the Outer South East and the South West, and also in four Mediterranean locations, reveal that many people leave London explicitly for reasons connected with their health. Moreover, the onset of ill-health or functional incapacity stimulates moves to live nearer or with relatives, or into institutional accommodation, particularly among those living alone. On the other hand, poor health sometimes retards or prevents a move, particularly among those living with a spouse or other carer.

The main effect of the social selectivity of the exodus of older people from London must be to lower the mean socio-economic standing of the city's older people in comparison with that of its working-age population. Given that the shift from being 'economically active' to 'retired' is itself a massive social transition, not least because income usually declines substantially, and given that patterns of household composition change greatly with increasing age through the retirement years, there are many difficulties in specifying the change in social composition. No detailed analyses are known. The possibility of a significant change does however mean that even if the social and health characteristics of London's adult or working-age population are favourable, it cannot be assumed that the descriptions extend to older people. On the contrary, the substantial migration exchanges make it possible for the older population of London to be relatively vulnerable and deprived.

5 The ethnic composition of London's older population

London has for centuries been the most cosmopolitan English city. Through the second half of this century, it has had by far the largest absolute and relative minority ethnic population of any British region (Jones, 1991). London's minorities may be dichotomised between the long-established Jewish and Irish communities, which have a 'normal' complement of older people and family structures, and the post-1950 immigrant (and descendent) communities from the Caribbean, Africa and South Asia which have very few older people. This characteristic will however change quickly.

The Jewish community of London has developed its own social care organisations and institutions, and the health and health care needs of its older members have been reported (Bowling and Farquhar, 1993). Mary Tilki (1997) of the University of Middlesex has prepared for this study a full account of the age structure, distribution and living arrangements of the Irish-born in London. Unlike other minority communities, the age structure of the Irish-born has an over-representation in the later working ages and the older age-groups. The mean age of those born in Northern Ireland is five years greater than the general population, and for those born in the Irish Republic it is ten years older. These differences may be partly explained by the irregular flow of in-migrants over many decades, but are an inevitable consequence of many of this population's children having been born in England.

Between 1981 and 1991, the Irish-born population of 60 years and over increased by 26.2 per cent. Only in the Borough of Brent are there high concentrations of the Irish-born, but they are found in all parts of the city. In 1991 there was a strikingly neat over-representation in all parts of the north west quadrant (Storkey and Lewis, 1996). There is a high prevalence of limiting long-term illness among Irish older men, who are unusually likely to be single, and their 'patterns of living ... have left many domestically unskilled and unable to be self-sufficient when frailty, poverty and illness occur.'

Most of the British minority ethnic groups have formed over the last four decades, to a large extent initially attracted here as 'migrant labour' and with the usual characteristics of such populations, i.e. strong initial over-representation of the youngest adult age-groups, few older people, and unbalanced sex ratios (Coleman, 1982). The latter feature has been variable, however, with the strong male over-representation in the early large migration flows (1950–69) diminishing and, in the Caribbean case, being replaced with female over-representation, partly reflecting employment opportunities and partly 'family completion' (Diamond and Clarke, 1989).

As the decades have passed, the settlement of successive cohorts, immigration restrictions and the multiplication of British-born descendants have produced a general demographic tendency for the 'labour migrant' characteristics to weaken and for less atypical age structures to form. Many in the 1950s migrant cohorts are now around or approaching the statutory retirement age: for the next few decades there will be substantial increases in London's population of minority ethnic older people. In addition, in some ethnic groups, declines in fertility (which will be marginally reinforced by improvements in longevity) have produced a tendency for 'demographic ageing'. More importantly for the family and social situation of minority ethnic older people, over several decades the proportions will diminish of those who came to this country late in life, who acquired neither the English language nor a knowledge of our health and welfare institutions, and who as adult migrants have an attenuated social network of siblings, cousins and juvenile acquaintances. On the other hand, the proportion will grow of those who have raised families in this country, have full citizenship in legal and practical terms, have extended kin networks here and associates from all stages of life.

The 1991 Great Britain census introduced a new question on ethnic group membership. The responses have been coded into nine minority ethnic categories for the published tabulations: Indian, Pakistani, Bangladeshi, Chinese, Asian Other, Black African, Black Caribbean, Black Other and the residual group 'Other Other' (OPCS, 1993a). These data have been supplemented in many studies by information from the *Labour Force Survey* and special purpose inquiries. The exceptional presence of minority ethnic people in London's population was demonstrated by the 1991 census returns (Table 2.7). One-fifth of London's population selected a minority ethnic membership on their 1991 census return, four times the share in Great Britain. The next highest share among GB regions was 14.6 per cent in the West Midlands Metropolitan County. The largest ethnic group was the Indian, who formed 5.2 per cent of London's population, and they were followed by the Black Caribbean (4.4 per cent) and the Black African (2.4 per cent).

Table 2.7 The minority ethnic population of London, 1981 and 1991

Area of birth (1981) Self-ascribed ethnic group (1991)	Persons by household head's birthplace (1981)		% of resident population (1991)		
	Inner London	Outer London	Greater London	W Midlands Metro. County	Great Britain
East Africa[1]	0.9	1.7	2.4	0.2	0.4
Caribbean[2]	8.4	2.6	4.4	2.8	0.9
Black Other			1.2	0.6	0.3
India	2.6	3.9	5.2	5.5	1.5
Bangladesh	1.0	0.1	1.3	0.7	0.3
Pakistan	0.8	0.8	1.3	3.5	0.9
New Commonwealth and Pakistan	19.4	11.8			
Chinese			0.8	0.2	0.3
Other Asian			1.7	0.3	0.4
Other Other			1.8	0.7	0.5
Total non-UK	34.4	20.4			
All minority ethnic groups			20.2	14.6	5.5

Sources: OPCS 1982. Owen (1996), Table 4.5

Note: The 1981 figures are thousands of persons by country or region of birth. The 1991 figures are percentages in the ethnic groups offered by the census enumeration schedule of that year.
     1. Black African in 1991.
     2. Black Caribbean in 1991.

Without exception, the minority ethnic populations of Great Britain are presently young, but almost certainly each has seen an increase in the average age and a slight rise in the proportion aged 60 years during the 1980s (change from previous censuses can be calculated only for birthplace groups). In London, older members of the minority ethnic population comprised (1984–94) 5.6 per cent of the total older population, exactly four times the percentage in the whole of Great Britain. The relatively large component of older people will be partly associated with the concentration of people of Caribbean origin in the capital. These entered Britain in large numbers from the mid-1950s, earlier than the peak flows of the other major minority ethnic groups, and their age structure is much closer to the national profile than the groups which followed.

London's minority ethnic population of older people is already large by comparison with the nation and will grow quickly. London's ethnic groups are also more diverse than elsewhere. One of the largest groups is people of African-Caribbean origin or descent, of whom many, particularly in the younger age-groups, are natives of London and choose the designation 'Black British' (Warnes, 1996). Black Caribbeans had the oldest age profile in 1991, with a mean age in Great Britain of 33 years, compared to 29 for the Indians, 24 for the Pakistanis, and 22 for the Bangladeshis. The very young age profiles of the Pakistanis and the Bangladeshis reflect mainly the more recent dates of their peak immigration (the flows are always dominated by young adults), and partly relatively high fertility.

In London in 1991, the population of older minority ethnic group people was dominated by Black Caribbeans and Indians with a bold contrast between the inner and outer zones (Figure 2.2). In inner London there were approximately 18,000 Black Caribbeans aged 60–74 years and 2,000 aged 75 years and over (OPCS, 1993a). Alongside were 5,000 aged 60–74 years in the Indian ethnic group and 1,000 aged at least 75 years, but in every other minority ethnic group only much smaller numbers. In outer London the most numerous group was the Indians, with 17,000 aged 60–74 years and 3,300 aged 75 years and over. Alongside were over 8,000 Black Caribbeans aged 60–74 years and 1,000 aged 75 years and over, but many fewer in all other minority ethnic groups.

The major ethnic groups have taken different distributions within London since at least 1971, and these distributions are evolving. Excellent maps of the distributions among the electoral wards of London have recently been published by Storkey and Lewis (1996). Broadly, the Black-Caribbean group is concentrated in inner London, particularly the boroughs of Brent, Hackney, Haringey, Lambeth, Southwark and Lewisham. The smaller

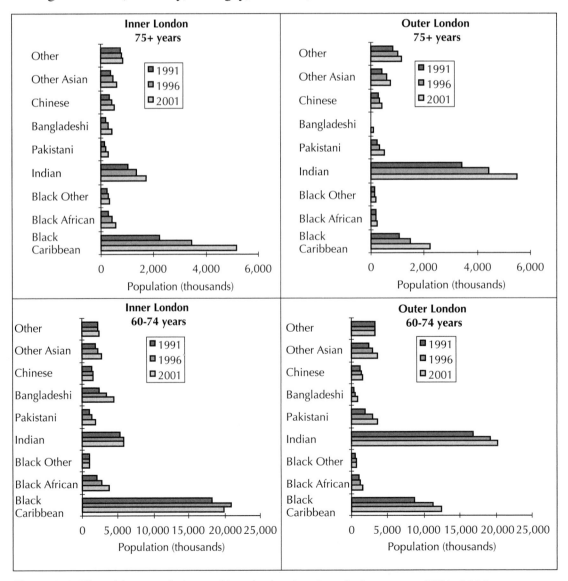

Figure 2.2 The older populations of London's minority ethnic groups, 1991–2001

(and very young) Bangladeshi population is concentrated in a single borough, Tower Hamlets. The Indians, a relatively large group, are clustered in three tight concentrations, in Harrow with Brent and Ealing with Hounslow (the two are barely separated), and on the borders of Newham and Redbridge. Pakistanis are most concentrated in three rather looser clusters, in Ealing with Hounslow, Waltham Forest and where Newham, Redbridge and Barking & Dagenham meet. The Chinese are generally in much lower concentrations, but an arc of relatively high densities passes from the north west of London each side of the Edgware Road, through Soho in Westminster and eastwards through Peckham, and Lewisham to Bexley.

Official projections of the numbers of people in the minority ethnic groups have not been attempted for good reasons. Apart from uncertainties about ethnic group and cohort-specific mortality, the out-migration rates of specific ethnic groups are not known. Another complication is that the declaration of membership of an ethnic group is a matter of identity or self-perception; for example, young Black Londoners are switching from self-ascription as Black Caribbean to Black British. The most important change now occurring in London's older population is, however, the increase of the number of minority ethnic people. It is helpful to produce estimates of the orders of magnitude of the expected changes, not only to inform health and social service commissioners and providers, but also to forestall exaggerations of the growth. A careful balance needs to be struck between raising awareness and jeremiad forecasts. The histories of the minority ethnic group settlements in London have created age structures that until now have been concentrated in the working ages. The numbers reaching the statutory retirement ages will henceforth grow quickly, with the highest rates of increase at the oldest ages. But for a long time to come, the absolute number of older people in the minority ethnic groups will be small, with lower shares than in the general population.

Indicative projections have been produced using a simple cohort-survival method. Taking the 1991 enumerated population in inner London and outer London in the five-year age-groups aged 50 years and over, their survival in 1996 and in 2001 has been estimated by applying the 1992 English life table (OPCS, 1994a). The age-group specific survival ratios have been decreased by 10 per cent to recognise higher mortality in the minority ethnic groups. The age-specific net out-migration proportions of the general London population have also been applied (Warnes and Ford, 1995).

The relative size and the relative rates of growth of the older population varies greatly among the different minority ethnic groups. In 1991, 30.7 per cent of the GB minority ethnic population aged 50–59 years described themselves as 'Black Caribbean', compared to 18.3 per cent of all age-groups. These indicative projections suggest for both the Black-Caribbean and the Indian populations of young older people that the high increases of the early-1990s will not be sustained during 1996–2001 (Figure 2.2). Indeed, the inner London projection is of a decrease in the number of young elderly Black Caribbeans, matching the trend in the general population. On the other hand, it appears that the very high rates of increase of the population aged 75 years and over will continue among both the Black Caribbeans and the Indians and in both inner and outer London. Higher rates of increase are also apparent throughout the decade in both the Pakistani and Bangladeshi older populations. The Pakistani older population is much more numerous in outer than inner London, whereas the Bangladeshis are strongly concentrated in inner London.

The new minority ethnic communities have very young age structures and diverse family and household structures. Among the communities of South Asian origin, three generation households are much more common than in the host community. This is usually described as a cultural trait, but part of the explanation for the large household size will be low incomes, and it is also possible that 'family completion' migration, by which parents join sons or daughters who entered London some time before, has been selective of individuals with care needs and of families with unusually strong kin ties.

6 Mortality in later life

The following sections review mortality and morbidity among London's older people. They adopt a sequence standard to British accounts and which reflects the idiosyncrasies of available data. The most detailed and representative information is still data on the incidence and causes of death collected as part of civil registration. They also have the merits of a long time series, for modern death registration began in 1837, and of comprehensiveness, so information can be produced for small areas even, as has been done for London, the electoral wards (Congdon, 1988). Also available to us are diverse hospital patient, community medicine and general practice contact data, but these are of variable completeness and quality, and all are essentially 'cross-sectional' snapshots of patients for the reporting period, normally the financial year. This remains the case even when the unit of recording is the episode rather than a consultation or contact. Population-based series have not until recently been collected apart from the death registrations and a decennial survey of general practice consultations (Alderson, 1975, 1984; McCormick et al., 1995). Unfortunately very few London GPs participated in the latter surveys, and no data for London can be released.

Recently, health questions have been introduced into several standing, representative national surveys, from the General Household Survey to the population census. There are also bespoke surveys which collect more health variables, sometimes with full physical health assessments. Many of these sources produce self-reported health scores and retrospective estimates of the frequencies of illnesses and of contacts with health providers. These are very welcome developments, but there remain considerable limitations, the most important of which for the present purpose is that most of the survey sources use samples which are too small to produce robust estimates for the older population in a region, even for one as populous as Greater London (Whitehead, 1987).

Death rates rise exponentially through later life and are higher for men than women. During the early 1990s in England and Wales, the rate for men aged around 60 years was 1.3 per cent per year, at around 70 years it was 3.7 per cent, and for those around 80 years 9 per cent. The equivalent series for women was 0.8, 2.2, and 5.7 per cent (Table 2.8). The unprecedently low force of late-age mortality in 'modern populations' is evident in the annual rate for women aged 85 years and over of 14.9 per cent. London's death rates are generally slightly lower than in the nation and much lower than in provincial large cities. However, in both 1992 and 1984 they were higher at ages 55–84 years for males, and at ages 55–74 for females than in the remainder of the South East Region or East Anglia. It is quite remarkable that at the highest ages, 85 years and over, London's age-specific death rates are so low. The female rate in 1992 of 140.2 per 1,000 was 0.96 of the South East Region rate. Both the male and female rates were the lowest in any region of the country, including East Anglia.

For around 30 years in many of the most affluent countries, mortality in later life has been falling much faster than ever known before, repeatedly upsetting projections of the numbers surviving to very great ages. London's older people have shared in these trends

Table 2.8 Age-specific death rates at the older ages, London 1992 and change since 1984

Area	Males				Females			
	55-64	*65-74*	*75-84*	*85+*	*55-64*	*65-74*	*75-84*	*85+*
A. 1992								
Greater London	**13.3**	**37.6**	**87.3**	**187.4**	**7.5**	**21.2**	**53.9**	**140.2**
South East	12.1	34.7	86.2	189.0	7.1	19.7	53.7	146.3
West Midlands M.C.	14.6	40.6	94.8	198.6	8.2	22.1	58.4	151.5
Greater Manchester	16.7	43.3	100.6	208.1	10.0	26.2	65.6	151.5
East Anglia	10.5	32.4	82.2	189.1	6.4	18.5	55.5	145.1
England and Wales	**13.4**	**37.3**	**90.1**	**193.9**	**7.9**	**21.5**	**56.9**	**148.8**
Scotland	20.6	52.0	110.6	221.5	12.2	28.3	68.3	177.8
B. Percentage decrease since 1984								
Greater London	18	12	10	4	17	6	5	11
Ratio to E&W change	0.8	0.8	1.0	0.5	1.0	0.6	0.6	0.9
South East	20	16	9	7	16	10	7	10
Ratio to E&W change	0.9	1.0	0.9	0.9	0.9	1.0	0.9	0.8
East Anglia	31	18	10	1	19	14	4	12
England and Wales	22	16	10	8	17	10	8	12

Source: OPCS 1986. *Mortality Statistics 1984. Area, England and Wales.* OPCS Series DH5 No. 11. Table 2; OPCS 1994b, *Mortality Statistics 1992: Area, England and Wales.* OPCS Series DH5 No. 11, Table 2.

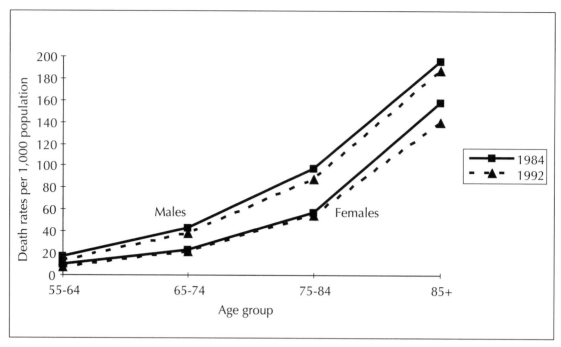

Source: OPCS (1994b), Series DH5 No 11, Table 2

Figure 2.3 Age-specific death rates for men and women aged 55 years and over in London

and with much the same variations by specific age-groups (Figure 2.3). Recent decreases in later life death rates have been greatest at the younger ages and somewhat higher for females (Table 2.8, Panel B). One difference between the male and female schedules is that whereas for the former, the improvement at the oldest ages for men has been the lowest, the female rates at 85 years and over have decreased markedly and more than around 80 years of age. Rates in London have been decreasing appreciably less than in England and Wales, particularly among females aged 65–84 years and among the oldest males. In passing, although it is often thought that because the decreases in later life mortality in Great Britain are faster for women than men, the task of combating premature mortality is greater among men. In comparison to many European countries, however, the relative excess of the English death rates is increasing much faster for women than men (Warnes, 1996b).

Boyle and Hamblin (1997) have recently published tables and maps of standardised mortality ratios (SMR) for the all-age and the under 65 years populations for the three status zones of London. Richard Hamblin has also calculated for this report the SMRs for the 65 years and over age-group (Table 2.9). The SMRs are based on deaths registered during 1989–94,[2] recorded by the normal place of residence of the deceased. The population base for the rates are the OPCS mid-year estimates for relevant years. The examination of SMRs specifically in old age is uncommon, for mortality variations

---

2   There have been delays in the publication of the normal series of mortality reports, affecting the data for 1993 forward: the first has just appeared (ONS, 1997). New coding practices have been introduced, including re-allocating all deaths to the year of occurrence, i.e. not coding by the year of registration.

are greatest at younger ages. Relationships between mortality and income, occupational status or 'deprivation' are stronger in the working ages than in later life when, as biologists have it, the 'force of mortality' is progressively exerted.

London's 'older age SMRs' show that after standardising for age structure, during 1989–94 males aged 65 years and over experienced 4 per cent fewer deaths per year than in England and Wales, and females had a 7 per cent advantage (Table 2.9, column e). As to the three socio-economic zones, the inner-deprived areas had a slightly adverse male SMR of 101, compared with 111 in provincial cities, but their female mortality rates were much more favourable, with a 7 per cent advantage compared to England and Wales (column a). The rates imply also a 12 per cent advantage over comparable provincial urban areas. The intermediate, mixed-status areas had lower mortality than the inner deprived areas and in comparison to the nation. They also had the greatest advantage relative to similar areas outside London (13 per cent for males and 15 per cent for females). Finally, the high status areas had low SMRs but rather surprisingly the female ratio to the non-London figure was higher than in both the inner-deprived and mixed-status areas. The male advantage in comparison to provincial high status urban areas was only 4 per cent, and the female advantage was little more at 5 per cent. Overall, the most striking feature of mortality among older people in London is how *relatively* low it is in the inner-deprived and especially the mixed-status zones. Across the three London area types, the variation in the SMRs is small for females and 2.5 times greater for males, but still much less than among the rest of the country (column i). This may be accounted for by their greater range of metropolitan, small town and semi-rural environments and populations.

Two questions are raised by London's mortality rates. Why are the death rates in London consistently lower than in comparable areas outside London, and why are the rates in

Table 2.9 Standardised mortality ratios, 65 years and over population, 1989–94

	London					Non-London				
	Inner-deprived a	Mixed-status b	High-status c	Range d	Total e	Inner-deprived f	Mixed-status g	High-status h	Range i	Total j
Males										
SMR	101	95	93	8	96	111	109	97	13	100
London/Rest	0.91	0.87	0.96	0.6	0.96					
Females										
SMR	93	91	94	3	93	106	107	99	8	101
London/Rest	0.88	0.85	0.95	0.4	0.92					

Note: The standardised mortality ratio is the ratio of actual to expected deaths, the expected number being calculated by applying the national age-specific death rates to the area's population age group. For a detailed explanation see Boyle and Hamblin (1997), Appendix 2. The standard 100 is for England and Wales.

London's inner-deprived and mixed-status areas lower for females than for males *relative* to provincial cities? The first question is normally answered by reference to London's social class composition. This is a shorthand reference to a host of differences, some of which can readily be demonstrated but others are presumed. The list includes childhood advantage, occupational risks, the 'standards of living' in the working and pensionable ages, nutrition and 'healthy and unhealthy behaviours', i.e tobacco smoking, alcohol consumption and exercise.

Substantial occupational and socio-economic differences are undeniable. The concentration of higher professional and managerial occupations in London is exceptional, and it has never participated in coal mining and hardly at all in the basic heavy steel or engineering industries (except along the lower Thames, with Ford's smelter at Dagenham and the 'White Country' belt of cement manufacture). But at the same time, London's population reports several adverse indicators which would normally produce late-age death rates closer to those of provincial cities and to the national figures. It has a substantial minority of very deprived people including the largest concentration in Great Britain of minority ethnic residents, many of whom were born and raised in third world conditions. Its housing conditions are poorer than in the rest of England. The rate of tobacco consumption is little different from that in the large provincial cities, and the prevalence of 'heavy drinkers' is higher than in the rest of the South East and East Anglia.

One hypothesis about the sex differential in the ratios of London's 'later life SMRs' relative to provincial cities is available. There is nationally a high male:female ratio among minority ethnic populations in the age-groups with the greatest frequency of deaths. This is found in the Bangladeshi and the Black-Caribbean populations, who are also concentrated in several of London's most deprived areas. 52.7 per cent of those in Great Britain who entered 'Bangladeshi' on the 1991 census ethnic group question lived in Greater London. Nationally the group has a most unusual age structure. Among the 11.1 per cent who were in their 50s and 60s, there were 2.4 males for every female (Owen, 1997; Warnes, 1997). Similarly among the Black-Caribbean population in Great Britain, whereas in most adult age-groups females exceeded males, among those aged 55–74 years there were 1.2 males for every female. Both the Black-Caribbean and Bangladeshi populations have significantly higher death rates than the general UK population (Balarajan and Bulusu, 1990). Although there has been convergence towards the general rates for several groups, 'mortality from coronary heart disease remains higher among men and women born in the Indian subcontinent, and highest in Bangladeshi men and Pakistani men and women' (Balarajan, 1996). This over-representation of male sub-populations with high mortality could account for a part of the sex differential in inner London's *relative* SMRs.

The comparative advantage of the oldest females in the inner-deprived and mixed-status areas is particularly strong. There are grounds for scepticism that the favourable death rates at the oldest ages entirely reflect true population differences, and a plausible hypothesis about the presence of artificial statistical effects can be developed. The exceptional mobility of Londoners has been demonstrated. When there are large population transfers across a boundary, there is always the possibility that the numerator and denominator populations entered into death rates are inconsistent. The question becomes, could the most elderly residential population of London be consistently over-estimated by the official statistical agencies? And under what circumstances would this effect be most pronounced for females and at the oldest ages? There are two possibilities. One is that in London more than elsewhere, there are older people and particularly females who appear in telephone directories, on 'council charge' lists and on census forms but are not full-time resident and have alternative addresses. When they become critically ill, those with alternative addresses might tend to leave the city. When they die, non-London addresses are likely to appear on the death certificates. The other possibility has similar reasoning but is more familiar. It is simply that our statistical collection procedures are not sensitive enough to pick up the net shift of very dependent and severely ill older Londoners to relatives' homes, to residential homes, and to nursing homes outside London. The new locations often become the 'places of residence' used for death registration (as when the former dwelling is sold), even if a common duration is a matter of months. The hypothesis is then that London exports some of its deaths to the rest of the country. It is not believed that these artificial effects explain more than a fraction of either London's apparent advantage in old age mortality or the relative advantage among the oldest females in inner London. It is, however, increasingly believed that such a fraction does exist.

7 The levels of disability of London's older people

As several of the most common physical and mental disorders have a prevalence that rises with age, it is usual to reason that demographic ageing leads to a rising quantum of disease and disability. Not least important is the increasing prevalence with age of multiple disorders and the complications of diagnosis, treatment and rehabilitation that they entail. However, age-specific incidence and prevalence rates are not constant. Successive cohorts have different exposures to risk factors: the decline in rates of tobacco smoking among males is now firmly linked to the decreasing incidence of lung cancer; and changes in occupations, conditions of work, domestic amenities, diet and exercise may all have impact on mortality and morbidity. Changed treatment practices and technologies alter not only the lethality of diseases but also their duration.

One focus of international interest has been whether disabled (or chronically sick) life expectancy is increasing more than healthy and active life expectancy (HALE). The reasoning is that new treatments, including more sensitive tests leading to earlier diagnoses, surgical procedures and drugs, are reducing the lethality of some disorders but not curing them, so that the sufferers survive longer but in states requiring treatment and nursing and social support. The British epidemiological evidence is however sparse and contradictory. Bebbington (1991) has estimated levels of age-specific disability using the GHS questions on limiting long-standing illness and extended these through to 1992 (Bebbington, 1995). He found that 'the trend in the ratio of health expectancy to life expectancy ... indicates no compression of morbidity' (Bebbington, 1991) and that 'overall there has been a relentless increase in the expectation of unhealthy life. For men it rose from 11.7 years in 1976 to 14.0 years in 1992; for women the corresponding increase was from 14.1 to 17.3 years. This seems to support the pessimistic view that we are likely to experience an expansion of morbidity and a consequent increased demand for health and social services as the population continues to age' (Bebbington, 1995). On the other hand, when the Katz Activities of Daily Living scale was applied by Margaret Bone to the responses to the GHS disability questions, 'health expectancy derived from these measures of mobility has increased in identical proportions to total life expectancy, with the result that the proportion of remaining years of life free of these disabilities has almost stabilised (during 1976–91)' (Bone *et al.,* 1995). Bone's assessment is that there has been no change during the 1980s in the prevalence of disability among older residents in private households and no clear evidence of a change in dependency among residents in communal establishments (cited by Kenny, 1996). It is of interest that the latest findings from United States research, which can draw on much larger national surveys with an impressive battery of health and dependency assessments, are mounting a substantial case that age-specific disability levels in that country are falling (Crimmins *et al.,* 1997; Manton, 1997).

The self-report variables on 'limiting' and 'long-term' illness of the census and General Household Survey are arguably too imprecise and subject to change over time to produce reliable time series, especially for a region of the country. Particularly over the relatively short periods employed for planning and budgetary purposes in the health and social services, the most important factors in the case-loads of specific services, or the size of institutional populations, are eligibility and assessment criteria and other policies, not changes in the morbidity and dependency status of the population.

The London Research Centre (Kenny, 1996) has estimated for this study the distributions of disability among London's older people by applying a procedure attributed to the Audit Commission (1992). The model applies the age and sex specific prevalence rates for ten levels of disability, as established by the 1985–6 OPCS Disability Surveys, to the

Table 2.10 Level of disability by amount of help needed

Amount of help needed	Severity of disability			
	1-4	*5-6*	*7-8*	*9-10*
A. Percentage who need:				
only a little help during the day or during the night	2	8	10	2
a lot of help or attention throughout day and night	0	0	1	18
a lot of help or attention throughout the day or throughout the night	0	1	8	33
help during most of the day with personal care, *e.g.* getting in and out of bed or toileting, but are alright on their own for an hour or so, and help most nights at least once for more than a few minutes	0	1	12	25
help occasionally during the day *or* during the night	1	13	30	16
Total: all who need help with self-care	3	24	62	94
B. LRC assignment to need categories				
Low need	97	76	0	0
Moderate need	3	22	78	24
High need	0	2	22	76

Source: Kenny, 1996a

projected population for London and its constituent areas (Table 2.10). The estimates assume no change in the age-specific prevalence of disability. A London weighting, based on the 1991 census reports of limiting long-term illness (LLTI), is used to adjust the national prevalence rates. Among those aged 65–74 years, the London LLTI prevalence was 0.95 of the Great Britain figure, and at older ages it was 0.96.

The linked concepts of impairment, handicap and disability are carefully defined and distinguished in this field of study. There are dangers in the retailing of crude numbers and, as the LRC report discusses in detail, in the translation of disability levels into dependency and need for social care and support. The variable care needs of people with different levels of disability are indicated in a cross-tabulation (Table 2.10). Disabled categories 1 to 4 are 'low' and generate very little dependency or need for care from others. One quarter of those with disabled severity in categories 5 to 6 are estimated to be dependent upon others for at least some care, 62 per cent of those in categories 7–8, and 94 per cent of those in categories 9–10. The LRC assigned appropriate percentages of those in the various disability severity levels to three need categories (Table 2.10, Panel B).

The estimated number of older Londoners in the various disability categories in 1996 is displayed in Figure 2.4 and the age distributions are shown in Table 2.11. For all Londoners aged 65 years and over, 56 per cent are estimated to be without disability, and 25 per cent have a moderate or high level (levels 5–10). It is estimated that there are 151,000 with moderate disability (levels 5–8), and 52,000 with high disability. The prevalence of the least severe levels of disability decreases with age and that of the most severe increases. There is a particularly sharp increase in prevalence from the early

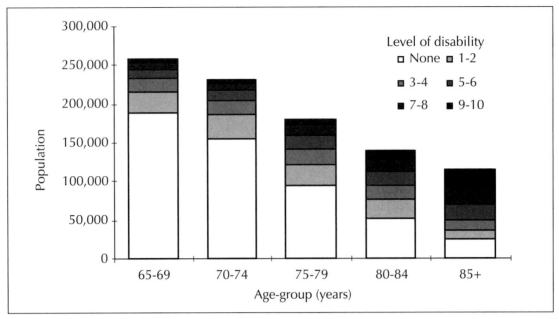

Source: Kenny, 1996a

Figure 2.4 Estimated number of older people by level of disability, London 1996

Table 2.11 Disability levels by age group of older Londoners, projected populations 1996

| | Disability level (percentage) | | | | | | Any disability | | | Pop'tn |
	None	1-2	3-4	5-6	7-8	9-10	000s	%	Score [1]	000s
65-69	72.8	10.9	6.6	4.6	3.2	1.9	70.0	27.2	3.93	257.3
70-74	66.7	13.2	8.2	6.0	4.0	1.9	77.0	33.3	3.91	231.3
75-79	52.8	14.3	11.1	10.1	7.2	4.4	84.8	47.2	4.50	179.7
80-84	37.4	16.6	13.3	12.9	11.5	8.3	87.0	62.6	4.91	138.9
85+	21.7	9.1	11.5	18.0	19.3	20.2	90.0	78.3	6.27	115.0
65+	55.7	12.8	9.5	9.0	7.4	5.7	408.9	4.3	4.77	922.3
65+ (000s)	513.4	117.8	87.5	82.7	68.7	52.2	408.9			922.3

Source: Kenny, 1996a

Note: 1. The score is a weighted mean based on mid-point of disability levels, excluding people with no disability.

80s to the oldest age-group. The table and figure show that in London as elsewhere, the great majority of older people aged less than 75 years and around one-half of those in their late 70s are without disability. At 80–84 years, only one-third have moderate or severe levels of disability, but at 85 years and over one-half have this level of restriction.

8 The health of London's older people

As levels of disability and dependency have steeply rising prevalence in the oldest decades of life, so also does the frequency of acute episodes of ill-health increase from late middle-age. A rounded understanding of older people's health and health care needs requires a composite picture, of the number of patients at different ages with acute episodes and of the number with multiple and chronic disorders. The exercise is complicated by the substantial reductions in the population 'at risk' with successive decades of life. The fact that there are very different rising incidence and prevalence schedules with age for various acute and chronic disorders makes it difficult to form an accurate, integrated understanding.

Only a fragmentary profile of the health of older Londoners can be assembled. The broad morbidity patterns of London's older people are not however expected to differ greatly from national patterns for which epidemiological accounts have recently been published (Carnegie UK Trust, 1993; Central Health Monitoring Unit, 1992; Medical Research Council, 1994). Several individual reviews of the health of older people nationally are available (Alderson, 1988; Grundy, 1992b; Tinker, 1992). Benzeval *et al.* (1992, chapter 3 on Morbidity) synthesised much useful information about the health status of all Londoners for the King's Fund's Commission on the Future of Acute Services. Several of their analyses of comparative causes of death describe the older population (for the vast majority of deaths from many causes take place in old age). They draw on the 1984–85 Health and Lifestyle Survey and find a common tendency for health symptoms to have lower prevalence in London than in the rest of England after standardising for age and sex. Consistent differentials between the healthier high status and the less healthy 'inner' (sometimes 'metropolitan') areas were also found.

The average number of physical illness symptoms reported in London was 2.8 per cent fewer than in England but 3.5 per cent higher than in the 'metropolitan' areas (Benzeval *et al.,* 1992, Table 3.3). The proportion of people assessed as unfit was 5.6 per cent lower than in England (op. cit.,Table 3.7). On the other hand, while all metropolitan areas had relatively high scores for psycho-social indicators of morbidity, London's scores were 6 per cent higher than provincial cities (op. cit., Table 3.4). They found higher levels of *limiting* disability but not *non-limiting* disability in London (op. cit., Tables 3.5 and 3.6). One summary measure, the percentage assessed as having 'poor overall health' produced quite high adverse indicators for London: a 12.5 per cent per cent excess in prevalence for all London and a 22.2 per cent excess for the 'metropolitan' (or non high-status) zones (op. cit., Table 3.9). They estimated that around 26 per cent of men aged 60–69 years and 35 per cent of women had poor health, and among those aged 70 years and over, 32 per cent of men and 50 per cent of women (Benzeval *et al.,* 1992, Figure 3.8).

Among causes of death, Benzeval *et al.* (1992) found a substantially lower incidence of deaths from ischaemic heart disease during 1985–9, which is corroborated by the 1989–94 data (see Table 2.12 overleaf). Cardiovascular diseases as a group are responsible for a lower proportion of deaths in London than in England or comparable provincial cities. 'Overall, residents of London districts have consistently and significantly less mortality due to circulatory diseases than residents living in England as a whole and comparable districts outside London. This is apparent for all comparisons of districts with given levels of deprivation, with only one exception – avoidable cerebrovascular

Table 2.12 Percentage of deaths from specified causes at ages 65 years and over, 1989-94

	London				Non-London			
	Inner deprived	Mixed status	High status	Total	Inner deprived	Mixed status	High status	Total
A. Males								
CHD	23	25	27	25	28	29	28	29
Ratio[1]	0.82	0.86	0.96	0.86				
Stroke	7	7	7	7	7	8	8	8
Other	70	68	67	68	65	63	64	63
B. Females								
CHD	21	22	22	22	25	26	23	24
Ratio[1]	0.84	0.85	0.96	0.92				
Stroke	11	12	13	12	13	14	14	14
Other	68	66	65	66	62	61	63	62
C. All ages and both sexes, 1985-89								
IHD Ratio[1]	0.76	0.81	0.92	0.82				
CVD Ratio[1]	0.75	0.81	0.86	0.80				

Notes: CHD Coronary heart disease. IHD Ischaemic heart disease. CVD Cerebrovascular diseases.
    1. Ratio of London percentage of rate to non-London rate for equivalent areas. Panels A and B were tabulated by Richard Hamblin. Panel C refers to absolute rates per 1,000 and is reproduced from Benzeval *et al.* (1992), Table 2.9. Their three socio-economic zones were inner-deprived, urban and high-status.

mortality in high-status districts – which shows no significant difference between London and non-London areas' (Benzeval *et al.*, 1992).

The very strong relative advantage among men in the inner-deprived areas merits further comment. The principal explanation is likely to be the much higher levels in the inner-deprived areas of provincial cities among the current older population of histories of manual, mining and heavy industrial occupation, and of heavy tobacco consumption and drinking. As discussed above, however, there is the possibility of an artefactual contribution, from mismatches between the numerator and denominator populations.

On the cancers, Benzeval *et al.* (1992) concluded that 'mortality due to cancer appears to be significantly associated with deprivation (and) non-Londoners on average have a worse experience of mortality than their counterparts in the capital. ... The only contrary finding is the figures for lung cancer in high-status districts, where the London rate significantly exceeds that of non-London.' On violent deaths they conclude, 'while there is significantly higher mortality due to road traffic accidents in districts outside London, the opposite is true of mortality from suicide ... due almost solely to the extremely high SMR [standardised mortality ratio] for suicide in inner-deprived London districts'.

Recently published papers have focused on trends in stroke mortality in London compared with the rest of South East England (Maheswaran *et al.*, 1997a, 1997b). These find that while standardised mortality ratios for stroke have been lower for Greater London than the surrounding region for the past 40 years, 'the situation regarding age-specific stroke mortality rates is more complex. The decline in stroke mortality has been slower in

Greater London. Very high stroke rates in London in the working ages are associated with deprivation and ethnicity – the Afro-Caribbean population have a 8–9 per cent higher incidence than the overall population.' The high stroke mortality extended during 1986–92 into the youngest pensionable ages. When adjustments were made for deprivation and ethnicity, the excess age-specific stroke mortality converted to deficit rates (Table 2.13). It is noticeable that the adjustment procedure has much greater effect on the younger than the older age-groups, reflecting the former's greater representation of the minority ethnic groups and, possibly, its lower prevalence of deprivation (although the authors warn that their four-variable deprivation measure may be insensitive to deprivation in old age). These findings are however a powerful demonstration of cohort changes in London's population. Not only are marked health outcomes shown, but also the clear implication of a changing pattern of need and of service requirements. These will manifest as the ethnic composition of London's older population changes, and if London's residential population is increasingly made up of those on the lowest incomes and with the least advantaged socio-economic backgrounds. The apparently favourable mortality and health status measures in the current population are no grounds for complacency.

9 Mental health

Epidemiological studies of mental health problems in older people have usually been carried out by psychiatrists on community samples selected using electoral lists, or by house-to-house surveys. One group of London GPs have carried out an epidemiological survey (Iliffe *et al.*, 1991a). Studies around the world have found consistently that the prevalence of dementia is a function of age. Hofman *et al.* (1991), reviewing 12 European surveys, found the prevalence at age 65 was around 1 per cent, but that it increased exponentially through approximately 5 per cent at age 75, 20 per cent at age 85, to 33 per cent of people in their 90s. This is close to the function described by Jorm's (1990) worldwide survey. Detailed age-specific functions of prevalence for London have not come to hand. Without these, any statement about the relative prevalence of dementia in London compared to the nation is hazardous (Table 2.14).

Table 2.13 Age and sex specific stroke mortality in Inner and Outer London relative to the rest of the South East Region, unadjusted and adjusted for deprivation and mortality, 1986-92

| Age group (years) | Males | | | | Females | | | |
| | Unadjusted | | Adjusted | | Unadjusted | | Adjusted | |
	Inner	Outer	Inner	Outer	Inner	Outer	Inner	Outer
55-64	1.59	1.16	0.85	1.02	1.30	1.05	0.77	0.97
65-74	1.14	1.02	0.84	0.95	1.08	1.02	0.84	0.97
75-84	0.95	0.93	0.86	0.92	0.89	0.91	0.86	0.91
85+	0.82	0.89	0.83	0.90	0.80	0.88	0.87	0.90

Source: Maheswarnan *et al.* 1997b. Table 5.

Table 2.14 Prevalence of mental illness among people aged 65 years and over in London

Area of London	Period	Sample	Dementia	Depression Males	Females	Anxiety
Lewisham and North Southwark	1986[1]	890				3.7
	1990[2]		4.7	15.9		
	1991[3]		4.6	13.4	25.3	
Gospel Oak	1994[4]					
Kensington, Chelsea and Westminster	1991-93[5]	3561	3.9[1]	5[2]	8[2]	8.5

Sources: 1. Lindesay *et al.* 1989. 2. Livingston *et al.* 1990. 3. Iliffe *et al.* 1991. 4. Blanchard *et al.* 1994. 5. Victor 1996.

Rates of alcohol use and misuse among older people have proved difficult to estimate. There may be reluctance to admit to over-consumption, or recall may be faulty. In general, it is thought that alcohol consumption is less prevalent among older people than among younger subjects. Iliffe *et al.* (1991b) found that 3.6 per cent of men and 3.2 per cent of women in their London sample exceeded recommended levels, and overall 10.5 per cent were daily drinkers. Long-standing misuse is associated with psychiatric illness and a family history of alcohol problems. Misuse which begins in old age is associated with bereavement, reduced social support and physical illness, and tends to respond much better to intervention (Kendrick and Warnes, 1997)

The high prevalence of depression makes it a major public health problem with high economic costs alongside the suffering it causes. The incidence of depression among older people has been estimated to be between 15 and 30 cases per 1,000 per year (Blanchard *et al.*, 1994). Unlike dementia, levels of depression vary little with age but there is a consistent sex difference, with approximately double the rate among women than men. Iliffe found in London a prevalence of 25.3 per cent in women and 13.4 per cent in men. The prevalence of depression varies between studies more widely than for dementia. This is probably associated with the various screening instruments which have different thresholds for 'caseness', but actual variation is possible. Depression is usually found to be more prevalent in deprived inner urban areas. Murphy (1982) found that the onset of depression in older Londoners was associated with major life events including bereavement, physical illness and financial problems. Vulnerability was increased by major social difficulties and the incidence of depression was higher in working class subjects. In addition, those without a confiding relationship seemed to be more vulnerable.

Symptoms of anxiety are very common. Specific disorders include generalised anxiety disorder, phobic disorders including agoraphobia, and obsessive-compulsive disorder. The diagnostic criteria are very strict and include only those people likely to need specialist psychiatric treatment. This may explain why the reported prevalence of cases of such disorders is low, at around 2–4 per cent of the over-65s. Lindesay *et al.* (1989, 1991) developed an assessment instrument that incorporated items from several scales, including the Geriatric Mental State. They reported that 3.7 per cent of their sample of people over 65 years old in Lewisham and North Southwark had general anxiety and 10 per cent had a phobic disorder. Agoraphobia tended to be of late onset whereas specific phobias tended to be long-standing.

Studies find that, on average, GPs identify only around half of the psychological problems among the patients presenting to them, and many older people suffering from depression receive no treatment of support. Blanchard and colleagues (1994) found in the Gospel Oak ward of north London that depression was associated with increased contact with GPs but that depressed subjects gave psychological reasons for consulting in only 3 per cent of attendances. Just over one-third of cases had discussed their emotional problems with their family doctors, but of these only half were receiving treatment with anti-depressants, psychotherapy or counselling.

10 Conclusions

In comparison with most parts of the country, London has a relatively low share of older people and their number will shortly be decreasing. This trend is likely to continue until the middle of the next decade. But the age structure of London's older population is unusually weighted towards the oldest ages, and the average ages of both older men and older women are greater than in the rest of England. The number in advanced old age has been increasing rapidly during this decade, largely as a consequence of cohort and migration histories, but this trend is abating and decreases are likely to set in as the century turns. London has the largest concentration of minority ethnic people in late-middle and old age. Among the nation's principal cities and regions, it will experience the fastest rate of growth of minority ethnic older people. This represents a considerable challenge to the flexibility of London's health and social care services and raises formidable tasks in the training of staff and for adjustments in day-care, residential and nursing home facilities.

Another distinctive feature of London is its massive population turnover by migration, which affects the older age-groups as much if not more than all others. The migration exchanges are sensitive to economic and housing market factors: broadly, the better the economy performs, the greater they will be. Considerable problems are raised by this turnover for projections of the health of the older population in the capital and their health and social care needs. The exodus around retirement age (and all later ages) is highly selective by income, socio-economic background and ethnicity. The persistent tendency must be to reduce the average 'material standing' of London's older population from that which would be predicted by the profiles of the working aged. The net result is complicated by differential survival, but it cannot be assumed that on average

London's older people are more advantaged or healthier than those in other provincial cities and certainly as compared with the national population.

Box 2.1: A primary care perspective on older people's health from inner west London

Christina Victor (1996) has recently analysed the morbidity information from the annual 75 years and over health check among GP patients in Kensington, Chelsea and Westminster. She speculates that the older people who remain in the area are among the more deprived, experience above average ill-health and poverty, and have less access to caring resources because of out-migration by younger relatives. The hypotheses were examined through the annual GP screening data. The Kensington, Chelsea and Westminster FHSA set up a pilot scheme in which specially trained 'link-workers' were employed to undertake the 75 years and over assessments (Young *et al.*, 1993). A lengthy interview schedule was developed, including 'a combination of validated screening instruments (as for anxiety, depression and dementia), commonly used questions (activities of daily living and self-report health questions), and new questions. Data were collected for 3,571 people aged 75 years and over from general practices throughout the FHSA for 1991–93.

The sample included 294 people in their 90s or older. Of the sample, 56 per cent lived alone compared with 48 per cent of those aged 75 years and over in Great Britain. Also in GB, 30 per cent of men aged 75 and over and 59 per cent of women lived alone, compared with 43 per cent and 70 per cent respectively in the sample. About 10 per cent of the sample lived in an extended family, with or without their spouse. Around 40 per cent of men and women aged 75–84 years reported good health, as did approximately one-third of those aged at least 85 years (Table 2.15). Two measures of chronic health problems were used: long-term illness, i.e. conditions present for 12 months or over, and limiting long-term illness, i.e. long-term health problems which restricted daily activity. Overall 70 per cent of respondents reported the presence of a long-term health problem, slightly higher than the 66 per cent for the 75 years and over age-group in Great Britain. There was no sex difference in the prevalence of long-standing illness, but limiting conditions were reported by 48 per cent of men and 54 per cent of women.

Table 2.15 Health problems among 75+ yrs, Kensington, Chelsea and Westminster, 1991–93

	75-79		80-84		85+		75+
	%	Ratio[1]	%	Ratio[1]	%	Ratio[1]	%
Males							
Health *not* rated good	56	0.95	57	0.97	68	1.15	59
Limiting illness	46	0.97	47	1.00	50	1.06	47
Fall in last year	24	0.84	30	1.05	36	1.25	29
Incontinent - urine	10	0.91	11	1.00	13	1.18	11
Incontinent - faeces	2	0.69	4	1.38	3	1.03	3
Dementia	4	0.77	5	0.96	8	1.53	5
Depression	8	1.09	6	0.82	8	1.09	7
Anxiety	12	1.29	8	0.86	6	0.64	9
Number	463		364		233		1060
Females							
Health *not* rated good	60	0.97	60	0.97	67	1.08	62
Limiting illness	51	0.95	55	1.02	56	1.04	54
Fall in last year	31	0.86	36	1.00	42	1.16	36
Incontinent - urine	18	0.95	18	0.95	21	1.11	19
Incontinent - faeces	2	0.47	5	1.17	6	1.41	4
Dementia	5	0.62	7	0.86	13	1.60	8
Depression	8	0.89	10	1.11	9	1.00	9
Anxiety	16	1.08	17	1.15	11	0.74	15
Number	861		867		753		2481

Note: 1. Ratio of age-group percentage to 75 years and over percentage

Falls had been common, more so among women than men. The prevalence of most of the health problems increased with age, but the gradients varied considerably. The self-reports of 'limiting' or 'poor' health had the lowest age gradients, consistent with innumerable reports of the greater tolerance, or lowered expectations, of health and fitness that accompany increasing age. The prevalence of affective mental disorders showed erratic changes with age, but only a weak overall age relationship. Anxiety had decreased prevalence in the oldest age-groups compared with 80–84 years. Dementia and faecal incontinence showed the steepest increases in prevalence with age. Most health problems were more likely among women than men of a given age, although the differential among the youngest (75–79 years) was much less than at the older ages (Table 2.16).

Table 2.16 Male:female ratios of health problems among 75+ yrs, KCW, 1991–93

	75-79	80-84	85+	75+
Limiting illness	0.90	0.85	0.89	0.88
Fall in last year	0.77	0.83	0.86	0.80
Incontinent - urine	0.56	0.61	0.62	0.58
Incontinent - faeces	1.00	0.80	0.50	0.68
Dementia	0.80	0.71	0.62	0.64
Depression	1.00	0.60	0.89	0.81
Anxiety	0.75	0.47	0.55	0.63
Average of above	0.82	0.70	0.70	0.72

Source: Victor (1996)

Chapter 3

The distinctiveness of London

Summary

- The housing amenities of older Londoners are marginally worse than in England as a whole but better than in provincial cities. Renting remains common in London. Apartments and sub-divided accommodation with poor amenities and access raise problems in low-income areas.
- The high mobility of London's population leads to attenuated local kin networks and a low prevalence of informal care. The average distance of an older person to the nearest child is relatively high.
- The detrimental effects of high property values are most evident in the markedly low provision of independent sector nursing homes throughout London.
- The scale and high density of development and commercial activity in London produces high land and property prices which increase the cost of providing new health and social care facilities.
- The division of London into 32 boroughs (excluding the City of London) for local government purposes and 68 NHS trusts raises the complexity of communication and liaison among both the various sectors of health and social care and between individual professionals and providing organisations.
- Given the distinctive nature of older people's morbidity and dependency, and particularly the relatively high prevalence of progressive, chronic and multiple disorders, older people's care is more likely than other age-groups to be damaged by flaws in the storage, retrieval and transmission of patient information.
- There is remarkably little information about patients' views of the system of statutory health and social care, as is most evident in the absence of patient-centred evaluations of the many investments and innovations during the 1990s in London's primary care.

1 The size, complexity and distinctiveness of London

The objective of this chapter is to highlight those characteristics of London and of its health and social services that are both distinctive and bear on older people's care. The focus is on the implications of the great size of the city: its high residential and commercial densities, the configuration and eccentricities of its current health service capacity, which often are a legacy of a distinctive evolution, and the administrative fragmentation of the purchasing and providing health and social service agencies. This chapter examines the characteristics of the city in relation to the health and social care needs of older people, keeping in mind both their relatively high prevalence of acute episodes, and the rising prevalence of physical and mental disabilities at the oldest ages. It provides only a broad picture and the distinctive details of the provision and the utilisation of specific services are reserved for later chapters.

The responsible bodies recognise that London's services are unusual and that problems attend. In 1995, in evidence to the House of Commons Health Committee, the Department of Health submitted that 'London's health service is not, at present, structured like ... a well-balanced, modern health service with primary care, general hospitals and specialist hospitals. Staff and resources are distributed over a large number of hospital sites and clinical experience is often fragmented. Primary care is underdeveloped in many parts of the capital' (phrases reordered, DH 1995). As one would therefore expect, London's statutory services attract frequent investigation and analysis, but with surprising inconsistency in the interpretations of the implications and the causes. At the end of the chapter, the various diagnoses and prescriptions will be reviewed.

The London population of 7 million in 1995 was by far the greatest concentration of people in Great Britain and more than 2.5 times greater than either Greater Manchester or the West Midlands metropolitan areas. Size alone confers advantages and disadvantages to the residents, not least older people. A selection of the most evident positive and negative impacts are set out in Table 3.1. One benefit of the unusually high population densities (although for more than a century the trend has been for lower densities), and of the resulting high demands for many goods and services, is that many facilities are correspondingly numerous. Such is the case for post offices, low-priced supermarkets, general medical and dental practices and pharmacies. The average distance from an older person's home to the nearest of these facilities must be short. Additionally, as public transport is exceptionally well developed in London, and people of statutory pensionable age are eligible for concessionary fares, access to services in general should be good.

On the negative balance, however, London's great size and its distinctive national functions bring intense competition for land, particularly in the inner areas, and great competition for residential space. One direct consequence is on the space and other conditions of London's housing. Space standards in London's housing are generally low, and although as in the rest of the country physical amenities have improved substantially in recent decades, the continuing poor housing conditions of a small minority of older people in sub-divided housing is indicated by the relatively high prevalence of 'without exclusive use of a lavatory' (Table 3.2). On this measure, the most severe deficiencies are in inner London but the problem is also present in outer London. On the other hand, while a higher

Table 3.1 Implications of London's size and functions on older people's housing amenities, on the provision of 'convenience' services, and on access to them

Disadvantages to older people	Advantages to older people
A. Housing factors and amenities	
High proportion of apartment and sub-divided dwellings with many access impediments for the less mobile and sub-standard heating arrangements	Large number of buyers for owner occupiers who wish to move
Low car ownership particularly in inner areas	
Very low provision of independent and voluntary sector residential and nursing homes	
B. Service provision and access	
High staff costs (wages, recruitment, turnover) particularly for intermediate grades and support staff	On average, short distance to most health facilities, especially general practice premises and pharmacies
Experienced professionals prefer to move to outer suburbs or beyond	Good public transport (underground, surface rail and buses)
Administrative fragmentation in the NHS and in local government (exacerbated by strong contrasts in political control and disposition towards statutory care) increases the complexity of communication between care sectors and professionals	Excellent range of specialist hospital clinics and expertise
	Abundant trainee doctors, nurses and paramedical staff

Table 3.2 Housing conditions among pensioner households, London and provincial cities, 1991

Area	Pensioner households (000s)	Without lavatory %	Ratio[1]	Without central heating %	Ratio[1]	Without car %	Ratio[1]
Inner London	300	3.5	2.2	28.5	1.2	72.5	1.3
Outer London	533	2.3	1.5	26.4	1.1	54.2	1.0
Principal cities	557	1.3	0.8	36.2	1.6	69.5	1.3
Other metropolitan	1,095	1.2	0.7	26.4	1.1	62.3	1.2
Great Britain	7,331	1.6	1.0	23.3	1.0	54.3	1.0

Source: 1991 Great Britain population census. Tabulated from small area statistics files held at the University of Manchester Computing Centre, see Warnes (1994), Table 6.

Note: 1. Ratio of the percentage in the area to the percentage in Great Britain. Households with at least one person of pensionable age. The principal cities are Birmingham, Glasgow, Leeds, Liverpool, Manchester, Newcastle and Sheffield. 'Other metropolitan' refers to the other districts of the Metropolitan Areas (formerly counties).

percentage of Londoners' pensioner households than in Great Britain as a whole have central heating in all rooms, heating arrangements are considerably poorer in the core authorities of the large provincial cities than in either inner or outer London.

Specific manifestations of housing pressure in London include the rapid conversion over the last two decades of mansion flats in inner-west London from renting to owner-occupation: this may be implicated in the especially rapid decline of Kensington, Chelsea and Westminster's older population. In the public housing sector, London boroughs have been particularly active in encouraging small households of pensioners to quit family homes and to move into flats and specially designed dwellings.

The elevated land and housing prices are the principal cause of high living costs in London. These are generally to the detriment of the older residents and to the provision of health and social services for them. Their own incomes are low compared with those of working age – for neither state nor occupational pensions have a London 'weighting'. Housing benefits will, however, reflect London costs and occupational pensions reflect prior earnings. A further consequence is that the cost of delivering all land and labour-intensive services (and particularly those with regulated wage and salary scales) becomes high. In the sphere of health and social service provision to older people, the most evident consequence of high costs is the very low provision of independent sector residential and nursing homes.

In many statutory services there is high *per capita* expenditure and high unit costs in London, as documented by Boyle and Hamblin (1997). High land and labour costs also make the construction of new health and social care facilities, from health day centres to hospitals on new sites more expensive than in most other parts of the country, and similarly, the modernisation of existing hospitals on hemmed-in sites becomes very difficult to finance. Whereas in a medium-sized provincial town, say on the scale of Norwich or York, a feasible option is to consolidate hospital services on a peripheral green-field site, to which the whole town can be reasonably served by buses and taxis, London does not have that option. It becomes particularly important to re-cycle existing plots of land in public ownership.

As became apparent in the discussion of London's population trends, the area of Greater London increasingly encompasses the functional urban area. This is better approximated by the 'London metropolitan area', extending to around 65 km from Charing Cross, which in 1991 had a population of 12.1 million. The pace of deconcentration of London's population has accelerated through the second half of this century, and Greater London is increasingly becoming but the core of a vast metropolitan area (Hall, 1989). The long-term implication of this perpetual process is that the dedication of inner London to the city's national commercial and administrative functions will increase. This will raise further the cost of dwelling space, and the population is likely to be further dominated by those of working age. However, the capital functions generate a large number of low wage personal service jobs (as in courier services, catering, office cleaning and transport), and these are frequently filled by recent immigrants to the city. The association of large parts of the inner city with disadvantage and low incomes is likely to endure.

The exceptional residential and social mobility of Londoners has been mentioned in several contexts. A consequence in later life is that the children of London's retired people are more likely to have moved away from the region than those from provincial cities.

This is largely a function of the elevated educational, occupational and income status of London families compared with the provinces. A related consequence is that when children marry and establish their own homes, on average they will move further away than in smaller cities. The greatest concentrations of new houses especially attractive to median income newly married couples are up to 40 miles away in Home Counties towns like Maidstone, Chelmsford, High Wycombe and Dorking.

2 The administrative complexity of London

London's local government has for over a century differed in detail from that in the rest of the country. A similar hierarchy of authorities has often been found, but a combination of population size and administrative exigencies have frequently lead to differentiation of the functions and financing of London's local government bodies. So it was with the Metropolitan Board of Works in the late-nineteenth century, and so it is now with the 33 London boroughs (including the City of London). On the other hand, the National Health Service has generally resisted the creation of distinctive organisational structures, agencies and providers for the delivery of London's health services. Whatever hierarchy of controlling, planning and providing organisations, or configuration of the sectors of care, has been implemented nationally has been applied to London. The consequence has been a plethora of organisations, often in the past with territories of responsibility that bore no relation to local government boundaries.

In contrast to the situation in several northern European countries including Denmark and Sweden, and to that which currently prevails in Northern Ireland, responsibility for the health and social services of Great Britain is divided between local authorities and NHS agencies. The social services serve five principal groups of clients: children in need of protection, those with learning disabilities, disabled people, people with mental health problems and dependent older people. The latter group includes many with physical disabilities, many who are socially isolated and/or have affective mental states, and fewer with psychoses or organic brain disorders. While close liaison between the mental health services and social services is clearly desirable for several of these client groups, physical health problems are likely to be most common among dependent older people. Arguably, therefore, the separation of responsibility for health and social care, if it does not work well, would produce most deficiencies for older people.

Several King's Fund reports produced in the early 1990s for the Commission on the Future of Acute Health Services and more recently for the London Commission provide details of the NHS structures and bodies (Boyle and Smaje, 1992; King's Fund, 1992). London's 16 post-1996 district health authorities and 68 acute, community and mental health providers are listed in Appendix 1 of *The Health Economy of London* (Boyle and

Hamblin, 1997). That report also maps the DHA boundaries and acute trust headquarters and satellite hospitals. The report on *London's Mental Health* maps both the London borough territories and the 27 'mental health trust catchment areas' (Johnson *et al.*, 1997).

There is considerable variation in the population served by the boroughs, the DHAs and health care trusts. The boroughs (excluding the City of London) range in population from 138,000 for Kingston-upon-Thames to 323,000 for Croydon, and the purchasing health authorities range from 240,000 (Hillingdon) to 729,000 (Lambeth, Southwark and Lewisham). Figure 3.1 illustrates the significant local purchasers and providers of health and social services as of 1994–95 to an older resident of each of four boroughs: Kensington & Chelsea, Redbridge, Southwark and Merton. The greatest contrast is between Redbridge, for which all acute, mental health and community health services are provided by a single NHS trust, Redbridge Healthcare, and Southwark, with two acute trusts (Guy's and King's College), a mental health trust and a community health trust. Another contrast is that in Redbridge, GP fundholders covered 44 per cent of the population, whereas in Southwark they covered only 14 per cent.

The difficulties faced by both providers and the general public in understanding who are the local providers and their respective niches are increased by the frequency of re-organisations. Since the internal market and the NHS provider trusts were established at the beginning of the decade, family health service authorities have merged with the health authorities, and the number of regional and district health authorities has been reduced. When added to the broken connections in information flow that are part and parcel of staff turnover and retirements, the information management task in London facing all sectors, but especially general practice, is truly formidable.

3 Administrative fragmentation and the health care needs of older people

The customary first points of contact with the health service and the subsequent 'routes' to more specialist treatment or convalescent and continuing care vary country by country. The NHS is distinguished by the importance of general practice as a normal first point of contact (apart from accident and emergency care). The GP maintains some details of a patient's records for all consultations, medications, investigations, acute episodes and referrals to other services. As on average older people have a higher frequency of episodes (if not clearly a higher frequency of consultations), and among the age-group are the patients with the highest prevalence of chronic and multiple disorders, they put a higher load than most on the information handling abilities of the general practice.

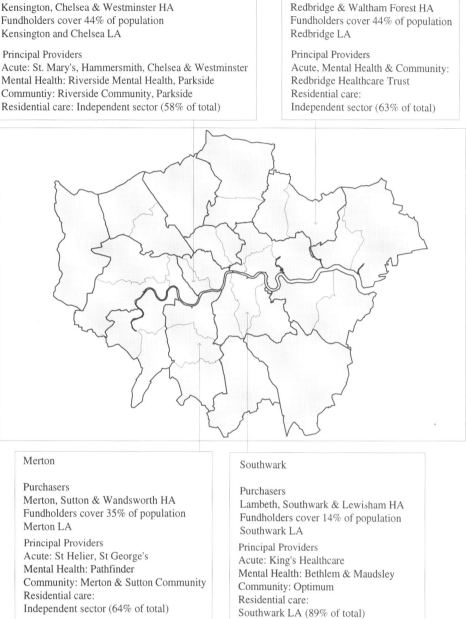

Kensington

Purchasers
Kensington, Chelsea & Westminster HA
Fundholders cover 44% of population
Kensington and Chelsea LA

Principal Providers
Acute: St. Mary's, Hammersmith, Chelsea & Westminster
Mental Health: Riverside Mental Health, Parkside
Communtiy: Riverside Community, Parkside
Residential care: Independent sector (58% of total)

Redbridge

Purchasers
Redbridge & Waltham Forest HA
Fundholders cover 44% of population
Redbridge LA

Principal Providers
Acute, Mental Health & Community:
Redbridge Healthcare Trust
Residential care:
Independent sector (63% of total)

Merton

Purchasers
Merton, Sutton & Wandsworth HA
Fundholders cover 35% of population
Merton LA

Principal Providers
Acute: St Helier, St George's
Mental Health: Pathfinder
Community: Merton & Sutton Community
Residential care:
Independent sector (64% of total)

Southwark

Purchasers
Lambeth, Southwark & Lewisham HA
Fundholders cover 14% of population
Southwark LA

Principal Providers
Acute: King's Healthcare
Mental Health: Bethlem & Maudsley
Community: Optimum
Residential care:
Southwark LA (89% of total)

Figure 3.1 The plethora of purchasers and providers of services for older people in four parts of London

Older people have high usage of medications and particularly multiple prescriptions from different physicians, demanding close attention to dosage and interaction hazards. Some older people through poor eyesight or illiteracy in English have more than usual problems in compliance with the regimens, and long courses of treatment lead to instances of less than thorough repeat prescribing. 'It is well known that the mechanisms of drug handling and response show changes with increasing age, and that these factors have contributed in the past to the unacceptably high occurrence of iatrogenic morbidity among elderly people' (Swift, 1989). The general point is that the nature of the episodes and disorders of later life pose special tests on the information gathering, storage and retrieval abilities of health professionals' and providers' administrative systems. When many professionals and multiple providers are involved, as is frequently the case with most of the common progressive disorders of later life, then to add administrative fragmentation, as in London, is a recipe for sub-optimal and inequitable care.

These problems are compounded across boundaries between the sectors of health care and between health and social services, at the level of individuals by professional 'distances' between different groups, and at the level of organisations by separate funding streams and ideological differences. Over the last few years there have been unwarranted inequities in access to 'care assessments', partly arising from different approaches among the boroughs to spending the community care budget, and partly from the diversion of the budget for other purposes.

4 Health and social services expenditure: the implications for older people's services

It has been argued that the sheer scale of London creates a plethora of health and social service organisations which are likely to be inimical to the quality of care of older people particularly when this involves referral between providers. There are other ways in which London's health and social services are distinctive, some of which might be implicated in deficiencies of statutory care. National Health Service facilities and staff provide not only health care under the NHS but also significant activity in medical education, training, research, and private practice. Each of these supplementary activities generates separate sources of income, as does the non-health utilisation of NHS property and estates. There are many complications in tracing the allocation of expenditure to different sectors of health care, to different specialties and to different age-groups, and these have been compounded by the NHS internal market.

The separation of purchasers and providers, particularly the flow of NHS Executive funds through health authorities and general practice fund holders to acute and community trusts (often across DHA and sometimes across RHA boundaries), and the creation of competitive 'cost centres' which exchange payments, has raised many difficulties in determining NHS expenditure for specific areas like London and certainly for its component districts. Boyle and Hamblin (1997) have examined several sources to estimate spending in London (and its three urban area type zones) in 1989–90 and 1994–95.

In this chapter, only the main points of NHS spending in London are repeated, with the overall aim of assessing whether the patterns of expenditure and provision include

Table 3.3 Expenditure by the major statutory health and social service providers, London and the rest of England, 1994/95

Item	London £m	London %	Rest of England £m	Total £m
DHA (health care related)[1]	3,222	17.9	14,739	17,960
FHSA	1,100	13.1	7,300	8,400
DHA + FHSA	4,300	16.3	22,000	26,300
Social Services[2]	1,595	21.3	5,908	7,503
Older people programmes[2]	*642*	*18.0*	*2,926*	*3,568*

Notes: 1. Excluding expenditure by Regional Health Authorities *The Health Economy of London,* Table 37
2. *The Health Economy of London,* Table 40.

intended or unintended biases for or against services to older people. Wherever possible, expenditure specifically on older people's services is examined. The sums disbursed for health services by the district health authorities and family health service authorities (which are now merged) are a good approximation of expenditure on NHS health services. In 1994–95 the London authorities expended £4.3 billion, 16 per cent of the total for England. Given the high land, wage, recruitment and transport costs in the capital, this share has rough parity with the 14 per cent share of the population in London. London's share of the major components of this expenditure varies substantially, however, with a high proportion (18 per cent) of the expenditure in England by DHAs overall and a low share (13 per cent) of national expenditure by FHSAs.

Boyle and Hamblin (1997) showed that London's share of expenditure on day care and 'other purposes' is less than its national population percentage. While day care services account for a small proportion of total expenditure, they are important for a needy group of older people, often on the margins of having to be admitted to residential care. On the other hand, there is a relatively high spend on community health services which, other things being equal, should be to the advantage of convalescing, chronically sick, and dependent older people.

Total expenditure in 1994–95 on the FHS in London was £1.1 billion, 13.1 per cent of the English total and therefore less than the population share. The expenditure on general medical services in London was £396 million, approximately 40 per cent of the FHS budget and 16 per cent of the England total. This has been boosted in recent years by London Initiative Zone funds, amounting to £43 million in 1994–95, most of which is spent on capital projects for general medical services. The combined expenditure of £439 million represents 17.5 per cent of the expenditure in England on GMS.

Expenditure in 1994–95 was exceptionally low on the pharmaceutical services element of the FHS budget. These cover principally payments for drugs prescribed by GPs and dispensed by community pharmacists. This component of medical services is of great importance to older people, who consume a large share of the national drugs budget. It has been mentioned that older people are particularly subject to the maladministration of prescriptions and the toxic side effects of drug interactions. Not only is the direct expenditure on the drugs important, but also the time and expertise devoted to the selection of prescriptions and the monitoring of their effects. One difficulty in evaluating this relatively low expenditure is that prescription drugs are also available through hospital pharmacies: the relatively high usage of acute services would suggest a correspondingly high expenditure by hospital pharmacies in London, even though this has been closely controlled in recent years.

The community health care NHS trusts established following the 1990 NHS Act were to play a role in stemming 'the drift towards institutional care that had been encouraged by the perverse incentives of the income (or residential home fees) support system in the 1980s. The intention of this legislation is to provide a level of social care – personal care and domiciliary care services – that enables frail elderly people to stay in their homes and avoids forcing a move into residential or nursing home care' (Howse and Dalley, 1996). This sector of social care is therefore of great importance to that category of older people who have a moderately high level of morbidity or disability. The domiciliary and day care services provide support to older people (and others) who have nursing or therapeutic needs but are able to live in private homes.

The community and mental health care NHS trusts in London in 1994–95 received 19.2 per cent of the expenditure in England but provided only 13.8 per cent of the national community service contacts. There is however inconsistency in the definition and recording of contacts across the country. There are also integrated health care trusts which, as the following chapter on utilisation will examine further, contribute to community service provision in London. When broken down by the major services for older clients, London's population received approximately national rates of service from district nurses, health visitors and (statutory provider) chiropodists, but substantially above average contact rates from speech therapists and dieticians. There is however considerable variation in provision by the sector of London, with little apparent relation to variations in need. Exactly the same proportion of community service contacts (81 per cent) was delivered at the clients' homes in London and in the rest of the country.

In 1994–95 the total expenditure of the social service departments of London's boroughs was £1,595 million, 21 per cent of the English total (Table 3.3). *Per capita* social services expenditure is some 60 per cent higher in London than in the rest of England, with the differential being greatest in the inner-deprived boroughs. They spent £323 per resident compared to £177 in the counterpart inner-deprived areas of provincial cities (Boyle and Hamblin, 1997). In contrast to health services, the main 'programmes' of

Table 3.4 Social services expenditure per capita of the 75+ years resident population: socio-economic areas of London and the rest of England, 1994/95

Sector of older people's provision	Inner-deprived		Mixed-status		High-status		London total	
	£	Ratio*	£	Ratio*	£	Ratio*	£	Ratio*
Residential care	720	1.67	392	0.91	373	0.99	471	1.27
Independent nursing homes[1]	120	0.80	89	0.75	83	0.88	95	0.87
Meals[2]	112	3.39	67	2.39	47	2.35	72	2.67
Home care[3]	541	1.71	365	1.41	303	1.42	389	1.61
Day (centre) care	118	2.31	68	1.79	63	1.91	79	2.32
All social services spending	2,163	1.73	1,322	1.18	1,107	1.18	1,464	1.51

Notes: * Ratio of *per capita* spend in London relative to that in the equivalent area in the rest of England
    1. Purchased care in independent nursing homes
    2. Meals-on-wheels and luncheon clubs (not meals served at day centres)
    3. Home helps and home care.

personal social services throughout England are organised by the age of clients, support for children claiming 26 per cent of the budget, and for older people 48 per cent (the other major programmes are for people with learning disabilities, physical disabilities and mental illness). Boyle and Hamblin (1997) have calculated the gross spending in 1994–95 on social services for older people *per capita* of the resident population aged 75 years and over. This has been done for the three urban area types of London and the rest of England and for six types of personal social service. The figures are tabulated in Table 3.4.

Overall, £1,464 was spent in 1994–95 *per capita* on older people's services in London, 1.5 times the amount in the rest of England. However, the disaggregation by service and area type shows that much of the differential arose from a very high level of comparative spending by the boroughs in the inner areas. The other boroughs spent just 18 per cent more than their counterparts in the provinces. Other details of London's social services for older people, including staffing and provision trends, are considered in a following section.

Throughout London, the provision of three services stand out as being most different: expenditure on meals is over 2.5 times as much in London than elsewhere, and in the inner areas nearly 3.5 times. Day care services receive more than double the funds *per capita* in London than in the rest of England, with again high expenditure by the inner boroughs – at nearly twice the rate in the rest of the city. On the other hand, expenditure on independent nursing homes is less *per capita* than in the rest of England, and lowest in the intermediate, mixed-status boroughs. The analysis of social services utilisation finds that the volume of clients in inner-deprived London does not match the high level of spending; rather, the contact hours delivered to each client are significantly higher than in the equivalent provincial urban areas.

Apart from the base funding of family health services, most sectors of the statutory health and social services which are used heavily by older people are funded at levels which are least equivalent to national *per capita* rates – some are much more generously funded. There are however specific services which receive below national levels of funding, most notably the hospital and community health day-care services. On the other hand, expenditure on local authority day-care services is exceptionally high in all socio-economic zones of London. The principal shortfall in the headings examined above is in public expenditure on the fees of residents in independent nursing homes. This is low in all parts of London, but particularly in the inner-deprived and mixed-status areas, with more than a one-fifth shortfall from the national level. On the other hand local authorities in inner-deprived London fund residential home provision relatively well, and may provide an adequate substitute for the less dependent category of nursing home residents. It would, however, not be acceptable for older people who need trained nursing care to be residents of homes without qualified staff only because of the absence of nursing home places. The low expenditure is undoubtedly because relatively few such homes operate in London. The implication is that there is additional load on informal carers and on the primary, community health and domiciliary personal social services.

5 London's hospitals as regional and national providers: implications for older residents

The most distinctive feature of London's health services is the concentration of prestigious teaching hospitals in the central and inner areas. The concentration has been noted for many decades and has been traced in detail in several accounts (Abel-Smith, 1964; Rivett, 1986). Decentralisation has been proceeding throughout the century. King's College Hospital moved from Portugal Street to Camberwell in 1906, and several of the innermost teaching hospitals have closed or decentralised in the last three decades (Charing Cross [1973], St George's [1979], Royal Free [1982]). The redistribution of the capital's hospitals has been repeatedly resisted and far less has been accomplished than required to equalise provision and access throughout the urban area.

The present situation is that the inner-deprived districts are 'over-provided' with acute beds (3.6 per 1,000 resident population), while the mixed-status and high-status zones are 'under-provided' (1.8–1.9 per 1,000) (Boyle and Hamblin, 1997). Interestingly, very similar contrasts are found among the equivalent zones of provincial cities, and the extent of 'over-provision' throughout London is clearer in a comparison of 'total beds'. No less than 44 per cent of the acute finished consultant episodes provided by the hospitals in inner-deprived London are however received by residents of other areas, a large proportion from the rest of London but also many from the surrounding South East. The complement is that the residents of London's inner-deprived areas have a low rate of hospitalisation.

Several proposed explanations circulate for this by-product of the distinctive and competitive nature of London's major hospitals – most are deep-rooted. The prime cause may be the regional role in the provision of elective treatments, which has enabled several medical specialties to achieve prominence and excellence in London, but which may have been to the detriment of general acute admissions and to the development of the 'care of the elderly' specialty. Another possibility is the importance of research and teaching in the London hospitals, particularly at the postgraduate level, and a third may be the relatively high demand and provision for private practice. Put at a more systemic level, a detrimental outcome for inner London's older residents might be predicted when several major teaching hospital are competing to secure the most prestigious clinics and advanced technologies while none individually has had an exclusive responsibility to serve a defined geographical area. The weakness in public health monitoring of the hospital services has been compounded by the division of London between four (now two) regions and among a profusion of district health authorities.

6 General practice in London

Another and contrasting view is widely held about London's health services: that the quality of primary care services is relatively poor. The deficiencies of London's primary care services, particularly in inner London, have been recognised for at least 25 years, and there have been several initiatives to correct them. A succession of inquiries and commentaries have established an understanding that London's GPs work from poor-quality premises, have a high average age and draw little support from practice staff. Less widespread, however, is an appreciation of the considerable changes that have occurred over the last decade, partly as a consequence of national reforms including the introduction of new contracts, fundholding and *The Patient's Charter*, and also from the London Initiative Zone management and training initiatives and investments in premises that have been special to London.

The problems first achieved national prominence when the 1979 Royal Commission on the NHS noted that in inner city areas, the service 'was failing dismally to provide adequate primary care' (Royal Commission on the NHS, 1979). This, with other studies, revealed high proportions of single-handed and older GPs, that few GPs were practising through group practices or from health centres; and that list sizes were low (DHSS, 1981; Jarman, 1981; Mohan, 1989). Other problems included: for patients, high population mobility and non-registration; for premises, poor standards and high costs; and for staff, the tendency for doctors to live remote from their practices, the high turnover of community nurses and paramedical staff, and the availability of more highly remunerated private work (Butler *et al.,* 1973; London Health Planning Consortium, 1981; Powell,

1987). Subsequent studies showed that at least some of these problems were shared in other inner cities, as in Manchester (Wood, 1983).

The Tomlinson inquiry of 1991–2 into the capital's health services found that '46 per cent of premises in the four inner London FHSAs are below minimum standards, compared with an England average of 7 per cent ... (and London has) twice the proportion of single-handed GPs, (and) a lower rate of employment of practice staff compared with other inner cities' (Tomlinson, 1992). Overall, the inquiry found, 'primary and community health services are comparatively underdeveloped in London. Resources need to be diverted from the hospital sector into these services in order to bring standards up to those found elsewhere and to enable the rationalisation of health services in inner London.' It recommended that £130 million should be made available to bring premises 'up to scratch'.

During recent years the London Initiative Zone programme has channelled substantial sums into primary care services in inner London which, with the introduction of purchasing consortia of practices as with the Central London Multi-fund, has stimulated the improvement and new construction of general practice premises, and the training and employment of practice managers, nurses and administrators. The diversity and vigour of recent initiatives is evident from the various health authority (formerly FHSA) primary care purchasing plans. There has been considerable investment in London's primary care premises. There have also been many initiatives to increase the support of the doctors from practice nurses and managers. Many observers suggest, however, that the staffing innovations are vulnerable to the cessation of the LIZ funds.

For example, Ealing, Hammersmith and Hounslow's plans for 1996–97 commented that 'an improvement in the number of GP practice staff has been a priority, in particular an increase in the numbers of practice nurses and practice managers. Whilst some additional staff have been funded there is now less uncommitted spend to achieve further improvements in the staffing levels.' The expenditure for practice staffing within EHH in 1995–96 amounted to £1.1 million for practice managers, £1.3 million for practice nurses, and £3.2 million for practice administration. Another example is from the Kensington & Chelsea and Westminster DHA *Primary Care Development Purchasing Plans 1997–98.* Among the points given prominence are that, 'a particular issue for inner city areas is to maintain a good supply of GPs willing to come in, replacing retiring GPs.' 'Communication between GPs and their patients is not always good and is often the cause of complaints.' A new practice-based complaints system was introduced in April 1996. 'KCW spends more per head of the population on GP support staff (practice nurses, practice managers, receptionists) than any other authority in the country. It invested an extra £400,000 in 1995–96, with a full year effect of £750,000 in 1996–97.' Figures are also provided on the characteristics of the practices in the health authority in June 1996 (Table 3.5). These show that the provision of GPs per 1,000 population approached the England and Wales average of 1991. However, the KCW practices remain deficient in terms of the number of principals per practice (implying a relatively high proportion of single-handed practices), and there are relatively few fundholders.

The most disappointing fact is that there is no evaluation of the impact of the many innovations and investments on the quality of the delivered services. We therefore have no information about the impact of recent changes in London's general practice upon London's older residents, either in the standard terms of consultation and contact rates, appointment delays, waiting times and other performance indicators, or in terms of the patients' perceptions of the service.

7 Personal social services

Kenny (1996b) has provided a wide ranging review and statistical compilation on *Trends in Social Services Activity, Staffing and Expenditure in Relation to Older People in London* . London's social services developed earlier and more strongly than those in most other parts of the country, but the 1980s and early 1990s has seen retrenchment in London and continued growth elsewhere. The expenditure trend has been downwards in real terms in all areas. 'The average yearly increase in gross local authority social services expenditure between 1980–81 and 1992–93 was 2.7 per cent in England and Wales and 1.5 per cent in London' (ibid.). The London rate of expenditure *per capita* was 1.8 times the level for England at the earlier date, and 1.6 in 1992–93. Subsequently, there have been increases in expenditure through the Special Transitional Grant for community care. The distribution formula gave lower grants to the London authorities than to others, further reducing the London differential in total social services expenditure to 1.5 by 1994–95 (ibid.).

Table 3.5 General practices in Kensington, Chelsea and Westminster, June 1996

	Population (000s)	GPs	Poptn/GP (000s)	Prac- tices	GPs per practice	Fund holders	Single- handed
Paddington	77	38	2.0	25	1.5		
North Kensington	47	36	1.3	19	1.9	2	
South Kensington & Chelsea	92	50	1.8	32	1.6		
Marylebone	57	39	1.5	18	2.2	13	8
Victoria	40	20	2.0	9	2.2	2	4
KCW	313	183	1.7	103	1.8	-	-
England and Wales 1991			1.9		2.8		

Source: National Health Service Health Agency Report Database

Kenny's summary findings on the domiciliary services are that the new community care system brought two main trends: an increasing concentration of services on fewer households, and a rapidly increasing role of the private sector. During 1992–95, contact hours for home help/care increased by 58 per cent in London and the hours per client household by two-thirds. The London rate of provision was 19 per cent higher than in England. The proportion of contact hours provided by the private sector increased from just over 1 per cent in 1992 to nearly 22 per cent in 1994. While meals provision to homes and in luncheon clubs decreased by a quarter between 1992 and 1995, the number of meals per person increased by a quarter. The trend to concentrate is also seen in the rising proportions of meals served at home and at the weekends. The London rate of provision is two-thirds higher than that of England, while the proportion provided by the private sector had increased to 18 per cent by 1994, overtaking the voluntary sector's provision and far exceeding the proportion in the country (ibid.).

Inner London boroughs employed 6.9 social services staff per 1,000 of the all age population in 1994, compared with 5.5 in the shire counties and 6.2 in the provincial metropolitan districts. The outer London rate of 4.8 per thousand is the lowest of all the local authority types – highlighting a massive contrast between the capital's zones (ibid.). Particular categories of staff were also examined, for example, inner London had 1.2 *social work* staff per 1,000 population, double the average provision in both outer London and England authorities. Another distinctive feature in London is that from 1984 to 1994, the total number of social services staff employed in London *decreased* by 12 per cent, whereas in England as a whole they *increased* by 12 per cent. The main decrease of 35 per cent was in the largest category – residential accommodation staff (ibid.).

8 Conclusion

London's size and economic, political and cultural importance implies several disadvantages as a residential area for retirement. Housing prices and rents are high, and while space standards and amenities have improved enormously in recent decades, they are still relatively poor in London, particularly in the inner areas. Specific problems are associated with the relatively large volume of rented property in sub-divided accommodation, and with deficient sanitary, heating and kitchen facilities. The high density of population has encouraged more multi-storey and high-rise dwellings than in most parts of England, which generates mobility problems for some older people. London also has advantages for retired people, among which the multitude and proximity of local services including general practice surgeries and pharmacies may be paramount. A relatively well-integrated (and regulated) public transport service is also of real benefit.

London may well suit many healthy and active older people but how do its health and social services perform for the age-group? One cause for concern derives from the great size of London's population. To provide both local government and NHS services, the city has been divided among a great number of purchasing and providing bodies. While it is true that in any part of Great Britain a dependent older man or woman who is eligible for domiciliary social services may be cared for by three health sectors as well as district social care staff, in London they are more likely to be served by agencies that do not have conterminous boundaries; neither do they necessarily have a mutual working relationship any more intensive than with several other similar bodies. This is particularly true of liaison between the acute trusts in inner London, which serve such a wide area, and the community health and social services. London's great size also implies that on average a hospital consultant will need to exchange information with many more general practitioners than elsewhere. This means the scope for communication gaps and administrative delays is great.

If there are weaknesses in the delivery of health and social services arising from London's scale and administrative fragmentation, many characteristics of older people's health problems, particularly their progressiveness, chronicity and multiplicity, suggest that they will manifest most clearly among this age-group. There is no research evidence about the general efficiency of communication among London's health and social care professionals when managing older patients and clients. Given that providers are so numerous and charged to meet internal performance criteria, it is remarkable that there is no intermediate level procedure (between the Treasury and the impressions of individuals) to monitor the performance of the health and social care system as a whole. Harrison (1997) has elaborated persuasively the case for system wide information gathering, audit, and interventions to improve the delivery of care.

London's health and social services are funded at above-national levels, but whether sufficiently to compensate for the city's high land, premises and labour costs is unclear. The funding of London's hospital services is especially high, much to support the regional and national roles in the supply of care and in training and research. Expenditure on providing services for the locally resident population is for many services close to national *per capita* levels. There are however marked deficiencies in the provision of hospital services to the older (and other) residents of London's inner-deprived areas, and in the availability of independent sector nursing homes. The overall picture for community health service provision is incomplete. Several specific services are provided at near national levels, but there appears to be considerable local variability. Personal social service provision is generally below national levels despite high expenditure, and a relatively low number of enrolled clients combines with above average hours of contact per client.

Chapter 4

Older people's utilisation of services

Summary

- Older people in London receive a large volume and wide range of health and social services, for the most part to a similar extent as in other parts of the country. In public health terms, no catastrophic deficiencies are found, although there are many specific weaknesses in the delivery of care that may lead to a poorer outcome in individual cases.

- It is not known whether the considerable recent investment and innovations in London's general practice services have left unchanged or improved patient care for older people. Several sources indicate that consultation and contact rates in London as a whole are at around national levels. Concern focuses on the quality and comprehensiveness of care in the inner-deprived areas.

- For patients at all ages above 50 years, many fewer acute hospital finished consultant episodes (FCE) are provided relative to the resident population of London's inner-deprived zones compared with similar areas elsewhere in England.

- The pattern is common to several specialties including 'care of the elderly'. If this finding is confirmed, then several 'knock-on' consequences for other services require urgent examination. It may be placing a heavier than normal load on the primary and community care and the domiciliary social services to care for the minority of older people, mostly in their 70s or older, who have chronic or multiple conditions.

- The adverse relationships would be exacerbated by the exceptionally low provision of independent sector nursing home places in London, again particularly in the inner areas. Such provision has been growing quickly in recent years, but not as quickly as in comparable provincial city areas or the rest of the country.

- The community health care services face special difficulties in London. They must liaise with many more acute trusts and social service departments than their counterparts in other parts of the country. They report during the early 1990s rapid increases in their case-loads, particularly of patients requiring the more intense levels of care. With other primary care services, they most work across the boundaries of care sectors and must find additional resources and expertise to provide the range and quality of services to the growing number of minority ethnic older people that the general population receives.

1 Introduction

This chapter reviews the provision of health and social services to the older residents of London. It aims to produce a synthesis with a focus on atypical features. It also highlights those aspects of provision that are a matter for concern, usually because utilisation appears low. Among these, most attention is given to features which are most evidently a consequence of either an intrinsic characteristic of the metropolis or a trait of its service organisation – the latter can more readily be corrected. The analysis relies heavily on the specialist reports commissioned for this study, on studies by Boyle and Hamblin some of which are published in *The Health Economy of London* (1997) and on other London Commission reports.

The health care needs of most older people are similar to those of other age-groups. There are some diseases and conditions especially associated with old age, and slow recuperation from illness is a common characteristic. A few diseases have strongly rising prevalence through old age, such as the dementias and osteoporosis. For the most part, however, older people's ill-health and acute health events stem from disorders and diseases that may occur at any age – disorders of the heart, circulation, joints and bones, blood, the digestive and respiratory systems, and the sensory organs. It is therefore necessary to examine all NHS services in the capital (with the exceptions of paediatrics and maternity), as all are used extensively by older people.

2 Population-based indicators of service use

A useful preliminary guide to the usage of various health services by older people is available in the 1994–95 General Household Survey and has been tabulated for this study by Evandrou (1997). The sample size in London allows only modest breakdowns by age-group or other characteristic. Among the population in London of 60 years and over, one-fifth of both the younger and the older age-group reported having visited their GP in the previous two weeks (Table 4.1). Although the proportions were slightly higher than in the rest of Great Britain, the differences were not significant at the 95 per cent level of confidence. Similarly the slightly higher consultation rate among women in London was insignificantly different from the male rate. A small percentage more had been a hospital outpatient during the previous three months, at rates very close to the national figure and with no statistically significant differences in London by age-group or by sex (although the GHS estimate was that 26 per cent of men aged 75 years and over had been outpatients compared to 21 per cent of those aged 60–74 years).

Many fewer had been hospital inpatients during the previous year, for only 10 per cent of the younger age-group and 18 per cent of the older reported hospitalisation. The younger age-group rate was 0.92 of the 13 per cent reported by people in the rest of Great Britain,

Table 4.1 Recent health service contacts among two age groups of older people by sex, London and rest of Great Britain, 1994/95

Health service contact	London, 60-74 years			London, 75+ years		
	%	95% c.i.	Ratio[1]	%	95% c.i.	Ratio[1]
Men						
GP in last two weeks	18.4	(12.5-24.3)	1.10	18.0	(7.4-28.6)	0.98
Outpatient in last 3 months	20.9	(14.7-27.1)	1.01	26.0	(13.8-38.2)	1.18
Inpatient stay in last year	11.7	(6.8-16.6)	0.90	24.0	(12.2-35.8)	1.37
Day patient visit in last year	8.0	(3.8-12.2)	1.42	8.0	(0.5-15.5)	1.71
Sample size	163			50		
Women						
GP in last two weeks	21.3	(15.2-27.4)	1.07	21	(13.0-29.0)	1.07
Outpatient in last 3 months	22.4	(16.2-28.6)	1.08	20.6	(12.7-28.5)	0.91
Inpatient stay in last year	9.2	(4.9-13.5)	0.93	14.7	(7.8-21.6)	0.80
Day patient visit in last year	2.3	(0.1-4.5)	0.50	3.9	(0.1-7.7)	0.78
Sample size	174			100		
Both sexes						
GP in last two weeks	19.9	(15.6-24.2)	1.08	20.0	(13.6-26.4)	1.04
Outpatient in last 3 months	21.7	(17.3-26.1)	1.04	22.4	(15.7-29.1)	1.00
Inpatient stay in last year	10.4	(7.1-13.7)	0.92	17.8	(11.7-23.9)	0.99
Day patient visit in last year	5.1	(2.7-7.4)	0.99	5.3	(1.7-8.8)	1.08
Sample size	337			150		

Source: General Household Survey 1994/95, re-calculated from Evandrou 1997, Table A.1.7
Notes: 1. Ratio of percentage for age-sex group in London to percentage in rest of GB. c.i. - 95% confidence interval.

but the difference is statistically insignificant. The utilisation by those aged at least 75 years in London virtually reproduced the national figure. The age differential in the both-sex hospitalisation rate in the rest of Great Britain, between 11.3 per cent at 60–74 years and 18.0 per cent at 75 years and over, is significant. There was also a sex differential in this measure, with 24 per cent of London's 75 years and over males reporting an in-patient episode, 1.6 times the female rate, although again the small sample sizes caution that these differences were not significantly different from each other or from the national rates. The national sex differential is insignificant.

The lowest utilisation rates in this set were as day patients during the previous year, with 5 per cent of both the younger and older age-groups reporting such contacts, close to the rate in the rest of the country. The estimates suggest that older men in London are day patients to a considerably greater extent than either women in London or men in other parts of Great Britain, and they suggest that the usage by London women was much less than elsewhere, but none of the differences is statistically significant.

Another GHS question elicited further indicators of people's contact with both the health services over the previous three months and the domiciliary social services over the previous month. The measures of health service use are consistent with the previous indicators which they amplify. Approximately one half of the older population reported a

Table 4.2 Recent health and social service contacts among two age groups of older people by sex, London and rest of Great Britain, 1994/95

Health or social service contact	London, 65–74 years				London, 75+ years			
	No.	%	95% c.i.	Ratio[1]	No.	%	95% c.i.	Ratio[1]
Contact with health services during last 3 months								
Doctor at surgery	107	52.5	(45.6-59.4)	1.09	67	46.2	(38.1-54.3)	1.00
Doctor at home	9	4.4	(1.6-7.2)	0.63	20	13.8	(8.2-19.4)	0.72
Nurse at surgery/health centre	29	14.2	(9.4-19.0)	0.89	23	15.9	(9.9-21.9)	0.85
Doctor at hospital	41	20.1	(14.6-25.6)	1.06	34	23.4	(16.5-30.3)	1.10
District nurse	4	2.0	(0.1-3.9)	0.75	15	10.3	(5.4-15.2)	0.93
Contact with personal social services during last month								
Social worker	1	0.5	(0-1.5)	0.39	4	2.7	(0-5.3)	0.79
Home help (local authority)	6	2.9	(0.6-5.2)	0.93	20	13.8	(8.2-19.4)	0.93
Private domestic help	7	3.4	(0.9-5.9)	0.88	11	7.6	(3.3-11.9)	0.64
Meals on wheels	1	0.5	(0-1.5)	0.53	7	4.8	(1.3-8.3)	0.88
Day centre	3	1.5	(0-3.2)	0.69	7	4.8	(1.3-8.3)	0.98
Lunch club	2	1.0	(0-2.4)	0.56	11	7.6	(3.3-11.9)	1.42
Sample size	204				145			

Source: General Household Survey 1994/5, re-calculated from Evandrou 1997, Table A.1.6

Notes: 1. Ratio of percentage for age-sex group in London to percentage in rest of GB.   c.i. - 95% confidence interval.

contact with a doctor at a surgery during the previous three months with a slight (but insignificant) indication of a higher fraction among the younger than the older age-group (Table 4.2). The national age-group difference in contact rates is not significant.

Around 14 per cent reported seeing a doctor in their homes (many of course do so as well as at a surgery), with a statistically significant difference between the 4.4 per cent contact rate among those aged 65–74 years and the 13.8 per cent rate among the older age-group. The estimated rates are substantially below those reported in the rest of Great Britain (where they are also significantly different between the two age-groups) but not significantly so. While therefore a direct comparison of estimates from London and elsewhere suggests that the capital's doctors are making around one-third fewer home visits to their older patients in London than elsewhere, the finding cannot stand until corroborated by other sources.

A primary care practice nurse was seen by around 15 per cent of London's older people during the previous three months, with little differential by age. The age differential in the remainder of Great Britain was found to be similar and also insignificant. The 15.2 per cent contact rate among those aged 65 years and over in London was 11 per cent lower than elsewhere, but the difference is statistically insignificant. Many fewer had seen a district nurse within three months but there was a very strong and significant age difference, from 2 per cent of those aged 60–74 years, to 10 per cent of those aged 75 years and over. Although the contact rate for the younger age-group was 25 per cent below that in the rest of the country, the estimates are of very small fractions of the population and thus the difference is insignificant. Just over one fifth of the London sample reported seeing a doctor at a hospital over the previous three months (without differentiation of in-patient from other settings). For the entire sample, the contact rate was 8 per cent greater than in the rest of the country, but the difference was not significant. The was little difference by age-group.

Turning to the personal social services, the overall picture is of much lower rates of contact and substantial differences between the younger and older age-groups. Very few of those aged less than 75 years receive any domiciliary service. This is much as in the rest of the country, although the London estimates are consistently below those for the rest of the country, yet not significantly so – the proportions are too low to claim such differences. Among the older age-group, the most prevalent service is local authority home helps, received by 14 per cent, a rate little different to the rest of the country. Just 5 per cent attend day centres and the same number receive meals-on-wheels: again, figures not significantly different from elsewhere. A higher proportion of Londoners reported attending lunch clubs than in the rest of Great Britain. Perhaps surprisingly given the comparative incomes and social composition of London's population and the under-provision of nursing homes, the estimated rate of employing private domestic help at 8 per cent was one-third less than in the rest of the country. The difference was not however statistically significant.

The overall pattern among older people living in private households (i.e. not institutions) is clear. There are frequent calls on the general practice services – in London the absolute number of patients consulting every two weeks turns out to be a quarter of a million (and some call more than once). And in 1994–95 around 14 per cent of London's older people, or 161,000 people, were admitted to hospital (although not necessarily in London). Many more, around 22 per cent or 278,000, were hospital and community health service outpatients during the year, but only a quarter of that number were day patients. Relatively few receive any personal social service, and those who do are aged above rather than below 75 years by a ratio of 3 to 1. Clients of the home help service are three times more numerous than clients of meals-on-wheels, and district nurses attend more of the oldest age-groups than attend day centres or lunch clubs. Among the listed health services, it is home visits from GPs and the district nurse service that are most oriented towards the oldest (and moderately and severely disabled) age-groups. Otherwise there is a clear contrast between the service provided by the primary health care and hospital services to all ages of older people (as indeed to all others), and the personal social services highly geared to a minority of those at the most advanced ages.

The following sections of this chapter examine the utilisation of specific services. The balance of material is inevitably conditioned by the availability of data and the detail and quality of different sources. The most voluminous information is for hospital episodes and the least comprehensive is for general practice. Nonetheless, it is appropriate to begin with the restricted additional information that it has been possible to compile for primary care. At the end of this sequence, further comments will be offered about the overall profile of health and social service use in London, together with an evaluation of the deficiencies and strengths of London's services, as indicated by their internal variability and by comparisons with the rest of the country.

3 Primary care

To provide some understanding of the comparative use of general practice services by older people and to document the growth in demand over two decades, resort is made briefly to national data. In mitigation, no significant difference was reported in the introductory section between usage by older people in London and the rest of England. With the exception of males aged 5–44 years and females aged 5–15 years, all age-sex groups of the population make large volume demands upon general practice. The 1991–92 General Household Survey showed that 12 per cent of all males and 17.5 per cent of all females had consulted a practice within two weeks (Table 4.3). The highest consultation rates are on the part of children aged 0–4 years. Apart from infants, older people do have the highest prevalence of consulters but not by a large margin, especially among females. For reasons that are not evident, males aged 65–74 years have a consultation rate (17.5 per cent) that is lower than females, whereas the oldest age-group of men have a rate (21.5 per cent) that exceeds the female figure.

Table 4.3 Consultation rates (%) with general practice staff in last 14 days, England and Wales

	Males			Females		
Age group	1972/ 1974	1991/ 1992	Growth % 1973-91	1972/ 1974	1991/ 1992	Growth % 1973-91
0–4	13.5	22.5	2.8	15.0	21.5	2.0
5–15	7.5	10.0	1.6	7.0	11.0	2.5
16–44	8.0	9.0	0.6	14.5	17.5	1.0
45–64	11.5	12.0	0.2	11.5	17.5	2.3
65–74	12.0	17.5	2.1	15.0	20.0	1.6
75+	17.5	21.5	1.1	19.0	20.0	0.3
All ages	10.0	12.0	1.0	13.0	17.5	1.6

Source: General Household Surveys

Notes: Consultations include those with practice nurses and paramedical staff and telephone contacts. Growth % is the average annual percentage rate of growth over the period.

The prevalence of consulters increased in all age-groups during the 1970s and 1980s, at 1.0 per cent per year for males and 1.6 per cent for females. Relationships between age, sex, and the rate of increase were intricate. Consultations by infants grew most. Among other males, those aged 65–74 years did show the fastest increase; but among other females, older people had markedly lower rates of increase than found among those aged 5–15 and 45–64 years. Women aged 75 years and over had by far the lowest rate of increase of any female age-group.

The decennial surveys of general practice in England and Wales collect a host of carefully differentiated measures of contacts and consultations with doctors and other practice staff, distinguishing the location, diagnoses and type of contact. It is most unfortunate that insufficient London GPs participate to enable separate tabulations for the city. The national age distributions of consultations in 1991–92 consolidate the emerging picture (Table 4.4). Very young children and those aged 75 years and over made the highest number of consultations in the years, around 5 for males, and among females, somewhat fewer among infants and 5.5 for those aged at least 75 years. These two age-groups also had the highest rates of increase during the 1970s and 1980s. The annual growth rates of around 1 per cent are however not high in comparison to those for other personal services. A further point of interest is that the sex differential in the number of 'doctor consultations' widened over the two decades, mainly brought about by the declining number of consultations by men aged 15–64 years. The selective delegation of tasks to other members of practice teams may be implicated. While both younger and older age-groups of men and women aged 60 years and over did show relatively high growth in their consultations compared to those of working-age, the differences are slim. It is certainly not the case that older people make massively disproportionate demands upon the service.

The decennial Morbidity Surveys record many other facets of general medical practice for older people. They demonstrate, for example, that home visits are disproportionately provided to the 75 years and over population, in line with the General Household Survey evidence. Doctors made 2.17 home visits *per capita* to this age-group in 1991–92, compared with 0.14 to those aged 16–64 years and 0.65 to those aged 65–74 years. Practice nurses made 0.065 home visits to the 75 years and over age-group, compared to 0.0009 and 0.0054 respectively to the younger age-groups.

4 Hospital utilisation

The substantial capacity of London hospitals in 1994–95 is reflected in their provision of 16 per cent of finished consultant episodes (FCEs) in England. That this is more than the proportion of the population of England living in the capital reflects the use of

Table 4.4 Consultations with general medical practitioners during one year per person, England and Wales, 1971/72 and 1991/92

Age group	Consultation rate			Ratio to both sex all-age rate	
	1971–1972	1991–1992	Av. annual change (%)	1971–1972	1991–1992
Males					
0–4	4.0	5.1	1.3	1.25	1.47
5–14	1.9	2.0	0.3	0.60	0.58
15–24	1.9	1.7	–0.5	0.60	0.49
25–44	2.3	1.9	–0.8	0.71	0.55
45–64	3.2	3.1	–0.3	1.03	0.88
65–74	3.8	4.3	0.6	1.21	1.24
75+	4.1	5.3	1.2	1.31	1.51
All ages	2.7	2.7	0.1	0.85	0.78
Females					
0–4	3.6	4.8	1.5	1.13	1.39
5–14	1.9	2.3	0.9	0.61	0.66
15–24	4.1	4.3	0.3	1.30	1.24
25–44	4.0	4.3	0.3	1.27	1.23
45–64	3.6	4.3	0.9	1.14	1.24
65–74	4.0	4.7	0.9	1.27	1.36
75+	4.5	5.5	1.0	1.42	1.57
All ages	3.6	4.2	0.8	1.14	1.21
Persons	3.2	3.5	0.5	1.00	1.00

Source: OPCS (1979). *Morbidity Statistics from General Practice 1971-2. Second National Study*, HMSO, London, Table 4; OPCS (1995). *MSGP 1991-2. Fourth National Study*, HMSO, London, Table 23.

Note: Consultations with doctor (not practice nurses) in 1991/92.

London hospitals by people living outside the capital. Turning to the use of acute hospital care by *older* Londoners, those living in inner-deprived areas appear to make less use than their counterparts in similar areas of England. They also use specialised hospital services for older people (the geriatrics or care of the elderly specialty) less than people in comparable areas elsewhere. Similarly low usage of general acute services has been observed among Londoners of all age-groups in the inner city (Boyle and Hamblin, 1997).

Table 4.5 FCEs per 1,000 resident population by five-year age-groups, 65+ years, 1994/95

Age-group (years)	Inner-deprived		London as % of non-London	Total		London as % of non-London
	London	Non-London		London	Non-London	
Men 65-69	378	424	89	374	344	109
70-74	453	521	87	453	425	107
75-79	575	636	90	560	531	105
80-84	641	746	86	647	626	103
85+	725	825	88	743	716	104
65+	489	552	89	492	461	107
Women 65-69	271	308	88	267	248	108
70-74	310	363	85	306	297	103
75-79	370	447	83	373	371	101
80-84	447	528	85	454	451	101
85+	557	604	92	541	509	106
65+	369	422	87	368	352	105

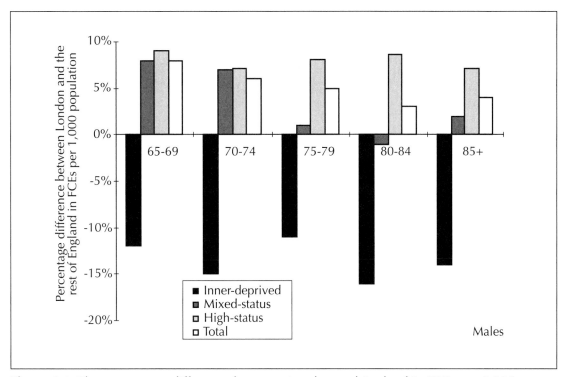

Figure 4.1 The percentage difference between London and England in FCEs per 1,000 resident population, males aged 65 years and over, 1994–95

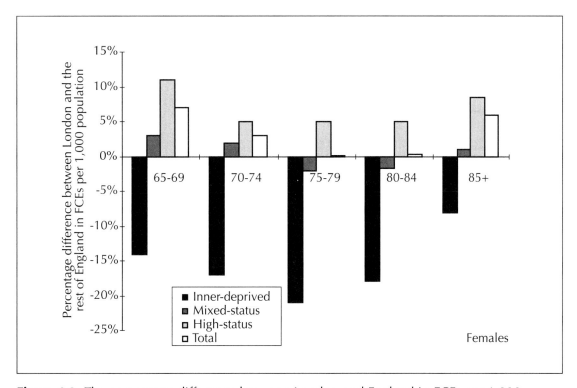

Figure 4.2 The percentage difference between London and England in FCEs per 1,000 resident population, females aged 65 years and over, 1994–95

Table 4.5 shows the number of FCEs per 1,000 resident population (based on the district of residence of the patient rather than the hospital) by sex for those aged 65 years and over. For all five-year age-groups above 65 years there are considerably fewer FCEs relative to the resident population of London's inner-deprived status zones when compared with similar areas elsewhere in England. However, the rest of London has higher *per capita* FCE rates than comparable areas outside, producing London-wide hospitalisation rates above national levels. The comparative hospitalisation rates of London and the rest of the country are shown in Figures 4.1 and 4.2. Again the consistently low rate of FCEs in the inner-deprived areas is the most striking feature. Also seen is the variation by age-group for the mixed-status areas.

This pattern of lower utilisation by older inner-deprived Londoners is accentuated when the number of hospital bed-days occupied by older people in 1994–95 are considered. Figure 4.3 shows considerably lower rates for all age-groups. This greater difference in use of beds in comparisons of similarly deprived areas when set beside hospitalisation rates reflects in this case a lower hospital length of stay and more day cases for London residents.

The four most common diagnoses among people aged 65 years and over in London are cataracts, acute myocardial infarction (MI), other chronic ischaemic heart disease and

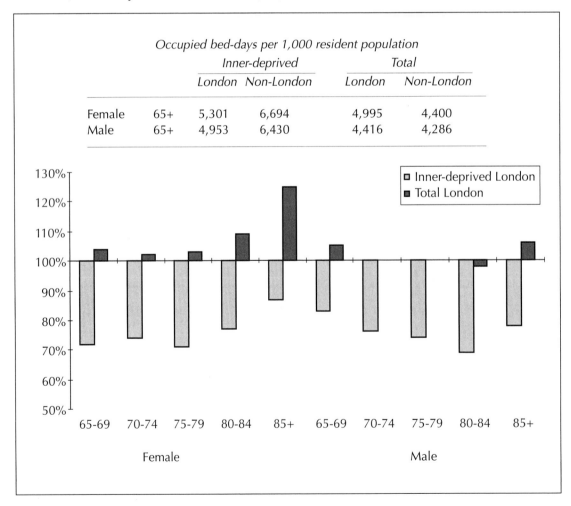

Figure 4.3 Annual occupied bed-days per 1,000 resident population in London as a percentage of comparable England figures, for people aged 65 years and over, by sex and five-year age-groups, 1994/95

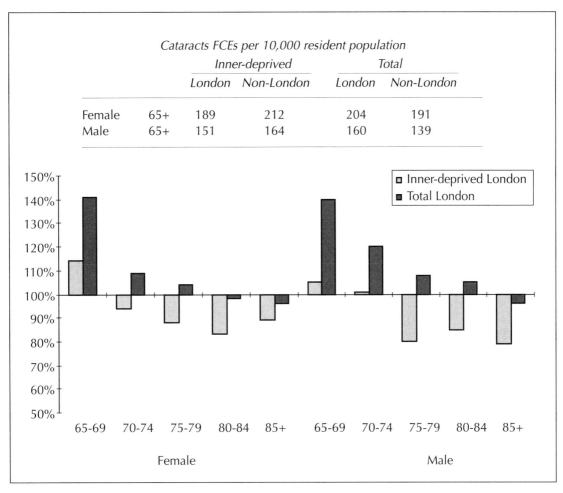

Cataracts FCEs per 10,000 resident population				
		Inner-deprived		Total	
		London	Non-London	London	Non-London
Female	65+	189	212	204	191
Male	65+	151	164	160	139

Figure 4.4 Cataract FCEs per 10,000 resident population in London as a percentage of comparable England figures, for people aged 65 years and over, by sex and five-year age groups, 1994/95

heart failure which together account for 34 per cent of all admissions in England among this age-group. The first of these, cataracts, is an elective procedure. The others tend to occur as emergencies. Taking first the cataract episodes, the rate among women aged at least 65 years is around 30 per cent greater than for older men in both England and London (Figure 4.4). Significant differences are revealed when inner-deprived Londoners are compared with their counterparts elsewhere. For most age-groups and both sexes, the rate in inner-deprived London is lower. It is of interest that an exception occurs in the youngest age-group of older people with its contrasting socio-economic profile. Males and females aged between 65 and 69 years have higher rates than the same age-group in the rest of the country. The extent to which earlier treatment compensates for the differential in later rates requires further detailed examination.

Turning to the three diagnoses related to the heart, the most striking difference is observed in the case of acute MI as Figure 4.5 shows. For inner-deprived older Londoners, hospitalisation rates for most five-year age-groups and both sexes are considerably below those in comparable areas in the rest of England. A similar though less extreme pattern of differences between older residents of inner-deprived London

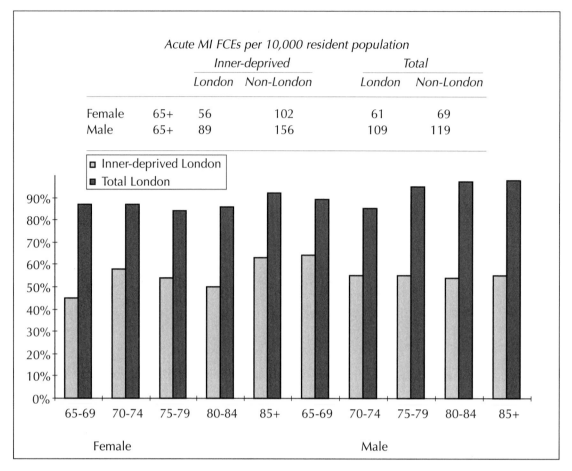

Acute MI FCEs per 10,000 resident population

		Inner-deprived		Total	
		London	Non-London	London	Non-London
Female	65+	56	102	61	69
Male	65+	89	156	109	119

Figure 4.5 Acute MI FCEs per 10,000 resident population in London as a percentage of comparable England figures, for people aged 65 years and over, by sex and five-year age groups, 1994/95

and comparable England areas is observed in the case of heart failure. No clear pattern emerges in the case of other chronic ischaemic heart disease. Differential access may be a factor here, although there is evidence suggesting that Londoners have lower mortality rates from these specific causes. Further analysis is required before firm conclusions can be drawn.

5 The 'care of the elderly' specialty[1]

'Geriatrics as a medical specialty was born in England in July 1948 when the first consultant geriatrician was appointed to the newly created NHS. From the beginning, geriatrics was recognised as a fully established specialty of medicine and this gave it access to resources and the right to seed its future growth by establishing formal training

---

1 As mentioned in the introductory chapter, terminological difficulties afflict this specialty, demonstrating that its labelling eschews scientific exclusivism and describes its patients somatically. 'Health care of the elderly' has widely replaced 'geriatrics' but late-1990s politically correct usage is substituting 'older people' for 'the elderly'. Objective survey evidence from the European Union claims that the preference of the age group themselves is to be descibed as 'senior citizens' or 'older people' (Walker and Maltby, 1997). The problems of nuance and changed meaning in translating terms into more than a dozen languages would be immense. Few have adopted Professor Sir J. G. Evans' decision, on the grounds that most of the specialty's patients are female, to rename the unit at The Radcliffe Hospital, Oxford, 'Geratology'.

programmes' (Evans, 1997). Proposals to establish the specialty can be traced to the early decades of this century in several European countries. They were taken up by Warren when working during the 1930s in the West Middlesex County Hospital at Isleworth (now in the Borough of Hounslow). Her seminal papers set out the principles of clinical practice among 'chronic aged sick' people and of the practical organisation of geriatric services that remain relevant today (Warren, 1943, 1946).

The specialty is self-evidently of special interest to this report. While it has been emphasised that the health and social service needs of the older population are not sufficiently described by the treatments and care the 'older people specialties' provide, and that the patients and clients of these services actually represent small minorities of people of pensionable age, their importance should now be stressed. The challenge to the physician of correctly diagnosing the patient with multiple chronic conditions is qualitatively different to the investigation of the aetiology of a single disorder. It requires a breadth of knowledge and assessment as well as depth. The goals of geriatric medical care are not only to cure, for that is not possible for many degenerative disorders and for pervasive physiological weakness, but to maximise the patient's physical functioning, independence, emotional well-being and self-esteem. These factors underpin the specialty's leaning to work in multi-disciplinary teams.

The principles of geriatric medicine have been formalised many times by medical colleges and professional associations. Two examples are given, the first from 20 years ago. The Royal College of Physicians (1977) argued the need for a specifically organised discipline of health care for older people, staffed by trained, committed and accountable physicians. The key items of their distillation of the principles in health care for the chronically sick older person are that:

- Diagnosis in the elderly may present particular problems because of insidious or atypical disease presentation and the existence of concurrent disorders.
- Assessment of physical, mental and social function should always accompany clinical diagnosis and treatment.
- Diagnosis and assessment require specialist skills supported by sophisticated diagnostic and treatment techniques.
- Organised professional teamwork with links to informal and formal agencies is necessary at all stages.
- The capacity of older people to recover from illness and regain complete or partial functional independence should never be under-estimated.
- The organisation and delivery of care should eliminate delay, minimise personal disruption and achieve continuity of information and professional contact.

The Royal College of Physicians (1994) has recently elaborated its views and set out the implications for commissioning bodies and providers. Grimley Evans (1997) has observed that 'in the past the cryptic presentation of disease in old age was compounded by social factors, including the stoical endurance of many older British people, to produce a high prevalence of unrecognised disease and disability. Whether this is still sufficiently true to justify some form of regular surveillance of older people is now under active investigation'. He also provides the most recent adumbration of the characteristics of disease in later life that need to be anticipated in the design of services and the practice of clinicians:

- *Calling for high quality diagnostic and treatment resources:*
  - cryptic or non-specific presentation of disease
  - multiple disease
  - rapid deterioration if untreated
  - high risk of complications of disease and treatment.
- *Calling for specific 'care of the elderly' expertise and responsibility:*
  - importance of social and environmental factors
  - complexity of comprehensive community care
  - economic constraints.

'Care of the elderly' services are unevenly provided across London. In 1994–95, 5 per cent of total London hospital activity was in the geriatric specialty. There were localised variations, with the geriatrics share being 20 per cent greater in the north central sector but 16 per cent less in north west London (Boyle and Hamblin, 1997). Variations by socio-economic zone were even greater. Overall geriatrics is an unusually small proportion of total capacity in the inner London hospitals.

Inevitably the variation is greater for smaller geographical areas, as shown by FCEs per 1,000 residents for district health authorities in Table 4.6. The array has been ranked and naturally groups into five DHAs – all north of the Thames – with rates more than 12 per cent above the England norm, three with rates at least 12 per cent below, and the remainder with rates ranging from 4 per cent above to 8 per cent below. Incidentally, Barking and Dagenham has an unusual elderly age structure, with a very large younger age-group and relatively few aged 75 years and over, a consequence of the massive public housing developments of the 1950s and 1960s. The effects of age-standardisation on the rates deserves close examination.

Table 4.6 Age-sex standardised rates of geriatric specialty hospitalisation, FCEs per 1,000 resident population, London district health authorities 1994/95

District Health Authority	Rate (%)	Ratio to England
Barnet	16.4	1.43
Brent and Harrow	14.8	1.30
Camden and Islington	14.5	1.27
Barking and Havering	12.9	1.13
Redbridge and Waltham Forest	12.8	1.12
East London and the City	11.9	1.04
Merton, Sutton and Wandsworth	11.7	1.03
Bexley and Greenwich	11.6	1.02
Bromley	11.2	0.98
Enfield and Haringey	11.1	0.97
Croydon	10.8	0.95
Ealing, Hammersmith and Hounslow	10.7	0.94
Hillingdon	10.5	0.92
Lambeth, Southwark and Lewisham	10.0	0.88
Kingston and Richmond	9.8	0.86
Kensington, Chelsea and Westminster	8.7	0.76
London	11.8	1.04
England	11.4	

The group with the lowest hospitalisation rates are seemingly unrelated. The low rate for Kingston and Richmond is initially surprising, for this DHA has one of the largest shares in the oldest age-groups, but the standardisation procedure would have corrected for this characteristic. The relatively affluent population may have more than usual access to private medical and nursing care. The fact that the geriatric FCE rate in some DHAs is one half that of others and the exceptionally low hospitalisation rates for the residents of inner-deprived London are causes for concern and deserve further examination.

Interesting differences emerge when the proportion of hospital care delivered to older people within the geriatric specialty is examined. Table 4.7 shows clear differences between the proportions for men and women, both in London and England. In London, there is less use of geriatricians among younger older people but more among the older, and women use specialist geriatric care more than is the case in the rest of England, whereas men use it less. Yet, inner-deprived areas of London stand out once again. Whether the differences shown here indicate better or worse care for Londoners is uncertain. It is clear that the pattern of care in London is different, especially in the inner-deprived areas.

6 Community health service provision

Utilisation of community health services is recorded through client rolls and contact data. Comparisons do require caution, however, for there is a degree of substitutability

Table 4.7 The proportion of hospital care delivered to older people by specialist geriatricians, London and England, 1994/95

	Age-group	Inner-deprived London %	Non- London %	London as % of non-London	Total London %	Non- London %	London as % of non-London
Female	65-69	3	3	77	2	4	63
	70-74	6	8	76	5	9	61
	75-79	16	15	108	18	20	90
	80-84	27	27	102	32	29	109
	85+	37	36	103	43	37	117
	65+	18	17	103	21	20	105
Male	65-69	3	3	97	2	3	66
	70-74	6	7	81	4	8	59
	75-79	15	13	121	15	17	92
	80-84	23	23	98	26	25	103
	85+	31	30	104	37	33	113
	65+	12	12	104	13	14	96

among different community health professionals, for example, some but not all employ specialist 'care of the elderly' and diabetic nurses. Contacts are often logged from many local offices and the diligence with which they are consistently defined and recorded has rarely been evaluated. The community health services throughout the United Kingdom show some consistent variations by type of area with, for example, inner urban areas returning the highest provision and utilisation and rural areas the lowest. However, there is also considerable variation within each settlement category.

The dominant community health services for older and younger patients are those provided by district nurses and health visitors. London has only slightly above the national rate of contacts when these two services are taken together (Table 4.8). Another relatively large NHS service is chiropody and the majority of contacts are with older patients. This service has exactly the national contact rate per head with the all-age population, but the 1,084 contacts in 1994–95 may also be expressed as a rate of 2.5 per 1,000 of the population who are 75 years, slightly below the rate of 2.7 in the remainder of England. Unfortunately the national contact data is not broken down by the age of the patients, and moreover there is no data for physiotherapists and occupational therapists (also important services for older patients), so it is impossible to pursue further a comparative analysis of provision (or utilisation). It should also be remembered that there is a significant element of private and voluntary sector provision of some services, including chiropody.

NHS chiropody contacts can be analysed by the area of London of the providing trust (Table 4.9). The rate comparisons are on the basis of the all-age population but nonetheless suggest that provision in inner-deprived London is 19 per cent higher than the national

Table 4.8 Community health service contacts in London and England, 1994/95

Community Health Service	London Number	London Percentage	England Number	London rate per 1,000 [2] Rate	London rate per 1,000 [2] Ratio[3]
District nurses	5,023	13.2	38,036	765	0.98
Health visitors	2,616	14.6	17,911	515	1.06
Speech therapists[1]	490	15.8	3,096	70	1.13
Chiropodists[1]	1,084	13.5	8,005	164	1.00
Dieticians[1]	379	18.2	2,082	52	1.27
Others[4]	729	12.9	5720		
Proportion of contacts in clients' homes	0.81		0.81		1.00

Source: Boyle and Hamblin (1997), Chapter 6, Key facts, p. 168.

Notes: 1. 1993/94. 2. Residents of all ages. 3. Ratio to rest of England. 4. Community learning disability staff, mental health nurses and specialist nurses.

Table 4.9 NHS chiropody contacts per 1,000 resident population, London and the rest of England, 1994/95

	Inner-deprived	Mixed-status	High-status	Total
London	195	120	187	164
Rest of England	196	178	157	164
London/Rest	0.99	0.67	1.19	1.00

Source: Department of Health returns KT23, 25, 29 and KC55-59 as analysed by Boyle and Hamblin (1997), *The Health Economy of London*, chapter 6, Figure 14, p. 177.

Table 4.10 Contacts per initial contact for five community health services, London and the rest of England, 1994/95

	Inner-deprived London	Inner-deprived Non-London	Inner-deprived London/Non-London	Mixed-status London	Mixed-status Non-London	Mixed-status London/Non-London	High-status London	High-status Non-London	High-status London/Non-London	Total London	Total Non-London	Total London/Non-London
District nurse	30	19	1.6	20	13	1.5	22	18	1.2	24	17	1.4
Mental health nurse	21	15	1.4	20	12	1.7	13	12	1.1	17	13	1.3
Speech therapist	10	9	1.1	13	11	1.2	12	11	1.1	11	11	1.0
Chiropodist	6.1	6.6	0.9	8.6	8.6	1.0	7.8	8.5	0.9	7.6	7.8	1.0
Dietician	4.2	3.7	1.1	2.9	2.9	1.0	3.0	2.9	1.0	3.4	3.0	1.1

Source: Department of Health returns KT23, 25, 29 and KC55-59 as analysed by Boyle and Hamblin (1997), *The Health Economy of London*, chapter 6.

Note: An initial contact is the first in an episode of care with a service provider in the financial year. Where a previous episode of care did not end with a positive discharge from care, a new episode is recorded only if more than six months have elapsed since the last contact.

rate for large cities, but no different from provision in provincial inner city areas. The other two zones of London show contrasting differentials with their provincial equivalents. The mixed-status areas have a contact rate one-third below provincial cities, while the rate in London's high-status areas is one-fifth higher.

Boyle and Hamblin (1997) have also analysed for the three urban area types of London the total number of recorded community health contacts for each first contact (*i.e.* the first contact in a financial year, giving approximately a contact rate per client), and for each 'initial' contact (i.e. the opening contact in an episode of care, giving an approximate contact rate per episode). The 'episode rates' tend for all five tabulated services to be close to non-London levels in high-status areas (Table 4.10). In London's inner-deprived and mixed-status areas, however, district nurse and mental health nurse 'contacts per initial contact' tend to be higher than in other cities. It should be emphasised that there are several weaknesses in the data and strong conclusions cannot be drawn.

7 Personal social services and community care assessments

The variation in social service activity can be glimpsed through data reported in the community care plans. 'Southwark reports that in 1995–96 it carried out 1,750 complex assessments (roughly 13 per cent of its population aged 75 years and over). Bromley reports that it conducted about 2,500 per quarter mostly of older people (and about 40 per cent of the population aged 75 years and over), and Hammersmith and Fulham made 624 complex assessments during six months. Such differences cannot be explained ... by the populations of older people' and seem to be determined by the size of the service and the way in which systems operate in each location (Challis and Pearson, 1996, paraphrased). Several boroughs have introduced service planning groups which have a membership of service users and carers, minority ethnic groups, voluntary agencies, health commissioners and providers and relevant borough directorates. Barking and Dagenham's community care plan reports 'consultation fatigue' which may been caused, it speculates, by the disappointment of raised expectations.

The community care plans, Challis and Pearson find, have 'plenty of evidence that the mechanics of joint working are in place and some signs that the spirit of collaboration is alive and well. It is less clear that (there is) much consistency in the ways in which need is thought about and quantified.' There are many developments taking place in London to fashion a system from the separated services. 'Joint working between health and social services is now commonplace, and the shift towards community-based approaches is well on the way. Concern about upgrading existing service stock is widespread and the challenges posed by mental health problems in old age are well appreciated. Needs assessment, however, is still in its infancy with a number of authorities having identified it as a priority for the coming years, and where assessment has been undertaken it is almost always of a service-based kind. ... Perhaps the most significant omission is the absence of translation of health-oriented information into plans. For example, there are almost no instances of the use of estimates of hip operations to predict the numbers of old people who may require help at home. Or, another example, almost no use of estimates of the incidence of dementia to determine the level and type of assistance which may be required. Furthermore, evidence of health promotion strategies is not used to create joint approaches to improving self-care.'

8 Mental health service provision

Philpot and Banerjee have recently reviewed mental health services for older people in London in the report *London's Mental Health* (1997) for the King's Fund London Commission. They concluded that there has been 'considerable progress over the past two decades in developing ... appropriate services for older people with mental illnesses in London (but) considerable variation remains across the city. There are examples of innovative services which maximise autonomy and provide high levels of home support, enabling patients to remain in their own homes as long as possible without excessive strain for informal carers. However, this quality and intensity of care cannot be matched in all parts of London.'

The development of hospital-based services has been substantial. A small survey carried out in 1983 found that at least seven London DHAs (of 20 who replied from a total of 31) had no consultant psychogeriatrician and only six had specific beds for the elderly mentally ill. The author's conclusion was that 'London districts virtually all appear to have poor services for their psychogeriatric patients' (Cunningham, 1983). By 1992, however, there were 51 consultants in London working full-time or part-time in old age psychiatry (Banerjee, 1993).

Table 4.11 Mental health FCEs from admissions to NHS hospitals: London, other inner cities, and the rest of England, 1994–95

Age group	Inner London [2] Rate	Ratio [1]	Outer London [3] Rate	Ratio [1]	Other inner cities [4] Rate	Ratio [1]	Rest of England Rate	Ratio [1]	England Rate
A. All mental health FCEs									
0-64	513	1.57	334	1.02	425	1.30	301	0.92	327
65-74	701	1.19	504	0.85	643	1.09	587	0.99	590
75+	1,125	0.80	1,018	0.72	1,339	0.95	1,478	1.05	1,411
B. Senile and pre-senile organic psychotic conditions FCEs									
65-74	146	0.69	172	0.81	227	1.08	210	0.99[1]	211[1]
75-84	620	0.75	639	0.77	872	1.05	869	1.05[1]	830[1]
85+	1,306	0.81	1,247	0.78	1,592	0.99	1,680	1.05[1]	1,604[1]
C. Other mental conditions FCEs (imputed)[5]									
65-74	555	1.46	332	0.88	416	1.10	377	0.99[1]	379[1]
75+	324	0.86	218	*0.58*	277	0.73	395	1.05[1]	377[1]

Source: Philpot and Banerjee (1997), Tables 6 and 7, p. 59.

Notes: 1. Ratio of 'Rest of England' to England interpolated from All Mental Health FCEs
2. The London Boroughs of Camden, City of London, Greenwich, Hackney, Hammersmith & Fulham, Islington, Kensington & Chelsea, Lambeth, Lewisham, Southwark, Tower Hamlets, Wandsworth and Westminster.
3. The London Boroughs of Barking & Dagenham, Barnet, Bexley, Brent, Bromley, Croydon, Ealing, Enfield, Haringey, Harrow, Havering, Hillingdon, Hounslow, Kingston, Merton, Newham, Redbridge, Richmond, Sutton and Waltham Forest.
4. The Metropolitan Boroughs of Birmingham, Bradford, Gateshead, Leeds, Liverpool, Manchester, Newcastle upon Tyne, North Tyneside, Salford and Sheffield.
5. Rates calculated as the difference between those tabulated by Philpot and Banerjee for categories A and B. The 75+ rates calculated using the all-London breakdown of the elderly population into 314,555 aged 75-84 years and 113,010 aged 85+ years (Boyle and Hamblin, 1997, Table 1-1)

Philpot and Banerjee present a commissioned tabulation of mental health FCEs by age-group of elderly people. This tabulates the rates of mental health FCEs arising from NHS hospital admissions per 100,000 of the resident population of two London zones, other 'central cities', and the rest of England (Table 4.11). They show that the very high rate of completed episodes in inner London among non-elderly people is not continued into the older age-groups, and that in both zones of London those aged 75 years and over have a substantially lower FCE rate than in other parts of the country. There is a low rate of FCEs throughout London for 'senile and pre-senile organic psychotic conditions' (roughly equivalent to the most prevalent dementias), in strong contrast to the provincial central cities. All the large city categories have substantial under-provision for these diagnoses, with the shortfall in inner London being the greatest deviation.

9 Residential and nursing homes

During the 1980s there was very strong growth in independent sector residential and nursing home places, stimulated by Department of Social Service payments for the fees. The ceiling fees and eligibility criteria changed frequently, producing fluctuations in the pace but not the direction of change. Under the community care provisions implemented in 1993 of the NHS and Community Care Act 1990, the new 'mixed economy' of residential care has been consolidated and further change encouraged, mainly in the negative way of withdrawing funds from local authorities to make their own direct provision. Trends during this decade have been complicated by the continuing effects of the late-1980s collapse of the over-heated property market. Many independent sector proprietors found themselves holding 'negative equity' or property assets, and all have found increased transaction difficulties, either in selling their own dwellings to finance the purchase of a residential home, or in selling on an institutional property they hold. The halting implementation of 'care management' with the transfer of the responsibility for fees to local authorities has not sustained the flow of placements.

The trends in London have been further confounded by the exceptionally high property prices and staff costs referred to in previous chapters. There is more competition for large villa properties in London than elsewhere, for conversion of the sites to modern apartments or for commercial uses. Another influence is the rapid rate of decentralisation of London's population. If no other factors intervened, the fast declines in the general population of the inner boroughs would be matched by similar reductions in the residential and nursing home population of older people. The 1991 Census established that London still had many fewer nursing home places *per capita* than either other large cities or the country as a whole (Table 4.12). As measured by the percentage of those 85 years and over who were placed in such homes, there were particularly large shortfalls in inner London. Only 6.3 per cent of the age-group were so accommodated. The share

Table 4.12 Residence in local authority residential homes and in nursing homes by elderly age-groups and urban area settlement types, Great Britain 1991

Area	85 + years in nursing homes		85 + years in other communal establishments		75 + years in local authority res'tl homes	
	%	Ratio[1]	%	Ratio[1]	%	Ratio[1]
Inner London	6.3	0.40	5.9	1.05	2.5	1.09
Outer London	9.3	0.59	5.3	0.93	2.1	0.92
Principal cities	10.6	0.67	6.6	1.16	1.1	0.49
Other Metropolitan	15.6	0.98	6.7	1.19	3.6	1.55
Great Britain	15.3	1.00	5.7	1.00	2.3	1.00

Source: 1991 Great Britain Census. Tabulated from small area statistics held on-line at the University of Manchester Computer Centre. See Warnes (1994).

Note: 1. Ratio of the percentage in the area to the percentage in Great Britain.

of outer London residents in this age-group in nursing homes was also much below the national level, and below that in the core authorities of the principal provincial cities. This under-provision in inner London was slightly compensated by above national rates of people aged 85 years and over living in other types of communal establishments – which includes almshouses and homes for older people managed by religious organisations (such as the large Jewish home off Clapham Common and several Methodist Homes for the Elderly). Similarly, there was a relatively large share of the 75 years and over population of inner London living in local authority residential homes.

The Health Economy of London provides several charts which illustrate the changing number of places in local authority and independent homes since 1985 (Boyle and Hamblin, 1997). By 1995, the number of inner-deprived area residents in all homes (local authority and independent) for older people was only 64 per cent of the total ten years earlier. In contrast, the number of residents in inner-deprived areas elsewhere increased by 4 per cent. However, in each case, the number of residents in local authority homes fell to less than half what they had been ten years previously. The difference between London and the rest of the country is accounted for by the change in the independent sector: while the number of residents of these homes in London increased by only 10 per cent in the ten years, in inner-deprived areas elsewhere, the number more than doubled. This pattern holds true for both mixed- and high-status areas. In mixed-status areas of London, the number of residents of all homes had reduced to 79 per cent of the 1985 figure, compared to a 33 per cent increase in equivalent areas elsewhere. The total number of residents in high-status areas had hardly changed in London, but the growth in similar areas elsewhere was 31 per cent. Clearly London's provision has become more deficient over the decade. In fact, the total number of independent sector places has declined relative to England by 65 per cent (Boyle and Hamblin, 1997).

Further detail is provided by Lewis and Glennerster (1996) in their evaluation of the implementation of the 1993 community care procedures in four anonymous London boroughs and an adjacent Home County. The boroughs were chosen 'to reflect a cross-section of authorities politically – some strongly supportive of the (former) Government's changes, others more traditional, and some marginal politically and in terms of their adherence to the mixed-economy model at the outset'. One was 'Conservative throughout ... supported a considerable commuter population and was prosperous (with a) population over 65 above average for its type'. The second was 'more typical of an inner-deprived area (with) above average social deprivation ... and a large public housing stock'. The third was 'also Labour (and) was much like many old-style country boroughs of the 1960s with a tradition of support for public social services, which it provided to a high standard'. As in the second borough, there was a very poorly developed private sector. The fourth was mixed socially and ethnically, 'it had higher than average rates of elderly people on income support ... and had a mixed political history'.

The authors do not claim that these boroughs are representative but they are a good cross-section and probably contain around one-eighth of London's population. The changing balance of the sectors of residential home provision from 1988 to 1993 is tabulated, and a selection of the figures have been entered in Figure 4.6. The columns represent the rate of provision per 1,000 residents aged 65 years and over. It is seen that the overall level of provision has remained around 83 places per 1,000 throughout the period. But the composition has changed quickly, with places in the boroughs' homes decreasing from 59 per cent in 1988 to 49 per cent in 1993, and the private sector's contribution increasing from 11 per cent to 25 per cent. Voluntary sector provision has been stable with the 30 per cent share in 1988 increasing to 33 per cent.

10 An assessment of the reviewed information

This review has gathered only a small fraction of the relevant information which could be assembled. However, many of the larger gaps could not however be completed with existing sources. Alternative sources of general practice data are becoming available. More comprehensive data on community health services could be brought together from the individual trusts, and similarly, much more could be learnt about the personal social services and the independent sector of residential care through the borough's social service departments and their registration and inspection offices. The largest gap of all is the absence of information from the patients or clients of the services. It is the customer perspective that is lacking in most discussion, appraisal and recommendations about the effectiveness of care.

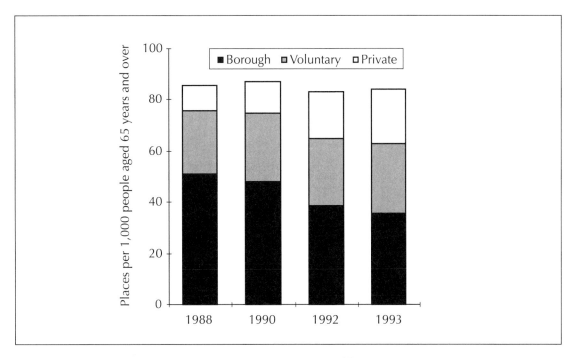

Source: Dept of Health, as tabulated by Lewis and Glennerster (1996), Table 6.1, p. 98

Notes: Residents aged 65+ in homes for elderly and younger physically disabled people per 1,000 population aged 65 years and over as of 31 March in the given years

Figure 4.6 The changing composition by sectors of residential home places in four London Boroughs, 1988–93

Where the patients' or clients' views are collected, so often the exercise is small scale and specific to a single service. There have been few, if any, attempts to monitor the performance of entire sectors of our health and social services from the customer perspective. Undoubtedly a rigorously designed and conducted study with an adequate sample, and over a sufficiently long period to capture the most common referral pathways and sequelae of health problems and care, would be an unusually challenging and expensive undertaking. As the entire range of health, residential and social services are so important to the entire population, and as they account in broad terms for 10 per cent of the gross domestic product (GDP) and for a larger share of employment, expenditure on 'market research' should be high.

11 The extent of collaborative working

The major acute trusts are increasing outreach services to local general medical practitioners. University College London NHS Trust's 1996/97–1998/99 Business Plan states that, 'The proper role of a specialist referral centre such as UCLH is to provide appropriate support to those delivering primary and secondary care. ... It follows that we cannot develop our services and define our role in isolation from others. We already liaise closely with local purchasers, GPs and patient groups to ensure we understand and can respond to their needs' (cited by Challis and Pearson, 1996). These efforts inevitably are largely hidden from the general public and are poorly understood in the media. Responding to a newspaper article, a Stockwell GP, the primary care manager for Clapham, and the chief executive of the Guy's and St Thomas's Hospital Trust on 31 May 1997 were moved to write to *The Guardian* that 'in south London, concerted action from a major teaching hospital, primary and community health staff has forged a commitment to deliver integrated and effective health care. We are beginning to see GP practices, primary care and hospital departments working together to build on the strengths of all providers and work through the inconsistencies. Change can happen without national frameworks and policies. It takes drive and enthusiasm from local primary care professionals, leadership, and a willingness to change on the part of hospitals.'

12 The obliquities of London's health and social services for older people

With a focus on the quantity, appropriateness and quality of the services provided to older people in London, two characteristics insistently claim attention. One is the high cost of providing services, particularly those with the highest relative employee costs. The characteristic stems from the intrinsic nature of a large commercial and capital city. Aside from uninhibited deregulation, which would include removing most controls on overseas immigration, which is inappropriate when competence and credentials are vital for maintaining the quality of medical and social care, only limited measures can ameliorate the ensuing problems. Several lie in the sphere of employee recruitment and retention, others in even more elusive aspects of staff morale: job satisfaction, progressive career structures, and of course remuneration.

The high land and property prices raise special difficulties in modernising and rationalising the system's premises. Given the enormous difficulties of finding and purchasing new sites, it would seem prudent to link the closure of large establishments with development plans. To find even the moderately sized plots that can accommodate a health centre and its car-parking demands is particularly difficult in London. The NHS in London could be supported by a range of cadastral and planning powers similar to those bestowed on the (private sector) railway companies in the nineteenth century or to those now orchestrated to enable airport construction and expansion. Some special measures would also seem to be justified to accelerate the provision of residential and nursing home care in London, particularly (as with so much else) in the inner ring of boroughs.

The other striking characteristic of the system from the older patient's point of view does manifest itself particularly in the inner zone. Innumerable pieces of specific evidence suggest that the composition or balance of the major care sectors is significantly different in the area that lies within 10 kilometres of Charing Cross from any other part of the United

Kingdom with a comparable residential population. On balance, it seems that general practice services are still on average sub-standard. Personal social services have very high unit costs and serve relatively few people but with puzzling intensity. The community care reforms have been taken up most unevenly among the boroughs, and large inequities in access to publicly supported care management now exist. Mental health services still lag behind those provided in other parts of the country, particularly given the concentration of needs in a metropolitan population, and maybe services for older people lag more than others. But most of all, it is the idiosyncrasies of inner London's acute hospital trusts that are a cause for concern. A high proportion of the older population require acute care in any given year, and by definition access to that service is often especially important – most of the population regard it in this way.

It is particularly important to gather more information about the very low rate of hospitalisation for acute FCEs among the residents of London's inner-deprived areas. Several issues need to be addressed. There is a possibility that statistical flaws account for some part of the presenting deficiencies. It is also possible that the exceptional roles of the major acute trusts in central London in serving a London-wide and the regional populations, and in education, training, research and private practice, distract them from sufficient attention to their local community function. The hospitals in question are, to an extent not found elsewhere, competitive for contracts, patients, prestige and their continued existence. Many consequences can be envisaged that would divert them from the treatment and care of the most deprived and inarticulate members of the city's inner area older residents.

Chapter 5

Synthesis and diagnoses

Summary

- A relatively high share of London's older people are in the oldest age-groups and the average age of Londoners aged at least 65 years is slightly higher than in the rest of England.

- The older people who remain in London are selective of the lower income groups, who experience above average ill-health and have below average access to informal carers because of out-migration by younger relatives.

- The most distinctive of the demographic characteristics of London's older people is the high representation of ethnic minorities, their diversity, the different distribution of each group within the city, and the imminence of high rates of increase among several of them. There is a low rate of referral of these populations to the community health care services.

- Alarmism in London's health and social services about the impacts of a 'demographic time bomb' is quite misplaced.

- Older people in London greatly value the National Health Service and the statutory social services but concerns about weaknesses in general practice, in hospital care and particularly the continuity of care are frequently expressed.

- There is no information about whether London's older people regard the general practice services they receive as having improved, deteriorated or remained much the same during the 1990s.

- An analysis of consultant episodes (FCEs) finds remarkably low rates of hospitalisation for the *resident* older population of London's inner-deprived zones.

- A number of issues have been identified which suggest the following deficiencies and causes for concern in the health and social services provided to London's older people:
  - low hospitalisation rates in inner London;
  - absence of evaluations of general medical practice;
  - the variability of community health care services;
  - low provision of mental health services for older people;
  - low provision of nursing home places in inner London.

1 On an older person's expectations of a city's health and social services

This chapter pursues further the integration and evaluation of the evidence presented in this report. One aim is to develop understanding of the connections which link (a) the characteristics of older people in London, (b) the distinctiveness of London's health and social service provision, and (c) the idiosyncrasies and problems of current provision and practice. Put another way, a prominent question is whether the special features of the capital impact for good or ill on the health and well-being of older Londoners and on the services delivered to them. Another focus is the problems and weaknesses of the individual sectors of care. The chapter lists those of most concern. All could be ameliorated or removed by a combination of changed policy and practice and (inevitably) increased resources within the existing organisational and professional frameworks.

Until the middle of the last century, large European cities were notoriously unhealthy places but thankfully those conditions have passed. The aspects of the relationship between urban setting and the health of populations that most concern us today are the organisation and delivery of care as well as access to it. This report has not resisted the attempt to identify ways in which London has more than its quota of a problematic group or an above average prevalence of debilitating conditions. But in some ways such exercises are diversionary. They take attention away from appraisals of the health and social services from a broad utilisation perspective. A contemporary comparison of the health of Londoners, Muscovites and New Yorkers would find sufficient differences of disease incidence and prevalence and in the ages and causes of deaths to fill a bulky report. Lengthy sections could also be devoted to lifestyles and 'healthy and unhealthy behaviours'. For most independent investigators, however, the dominant theme would be the great contrasts in the organisation of health care and social services and how they are accessed and paid for (Maxwell, 1993). Their evaluation criteria would encapsulate ideal models of service provision, of course with differences according to the author's social philosophies and political views, but for most permeated with notions of 'cradle to grave care', equitable access, treatment and care according to need, maximising the effectiveness of care, and improving the public health.

The focus of this report on older people and the services they use underlines the importance of a patient or customer-oriented evaluation. The quality and cost of health and social services are very important in later life. Not only does advanced age bring a relatively high incidence of health problems, ill health is especially threatening on two counts. Being aware of our own mortality or finitude, in the advanced years any problem is a potential threat to our continued survival. Secondly, many of the common disorders compromise functioning or are disabling. We fear the health problems that bring restrictions on our customary activities, and that bring incompetence and dependence on others. People dread becoming a burden on others.

The vulnerabilities of later life and these attitudinal responses mould the older population's hopes and expectations for the health and social services. If those of us who are not old push to one side the mainly physiological construction of older people's ill-health that we normally apply, and adopt instead an empathetic view, it is quickly seen why older people tend to attach great importance to every sector of health and social care. Jill Russell and collaborators (1994) have reviewed substantial research evidence on people's views of the NHS in London, including questions on the OPCS omnibus surveys commissioned by the King's Fund (Judge and Solomon, 1993). Interestingly, Russell *et al.*'s first summary 'key theme' was that, 'participants want policy-makers and service providers to give greater recognition to the inter-relationships between primary care and secondary care, between health and social care and between various specialist health services, so that patients can receive a 'seamless' or "holistic" service. ... Group discussions with elderly people and those caring for elderly relatives emphasised the importance of a continuum of care and support'. They also analysed variations in opinion by age, sex, class and ethnic group, finding that 'many of the views ... were shared by participants of all ages (and that) the assumption that a "gratitude barrier" exists among older people, making them more reluctant to criticise the NHS, was unsubstantiated'.

A recent addition to the evidence is Kate Mortimer's (1996) report, commissioned for the Older People Study, on older people's views of local health services in London as expressed through six focus groups, each in a different different DHA. A forcibly made point by several participants is a useful benchmark. The NHS is much valued among older people who still make comparisons with the health care system they experienced before: 'When I think back to the awful times we had, I only wish there'd been a NHS when I was young.' The focus group in East London & City HA made many complaints of poorly administered appointments systems in general practices and reported that 'where there are lengthy waits to see the GP ... some people leave and take themselves instead to A&E'. A repeated expression was that, 'Doctors were perceived as poor communicators. They did not keep patients properly informed and the onus was placed on individuals, providing they had the confidence and ability to ask. This was a particular problem in hospitals where patients saw many junior doctors but rarely saw the consultant ... patients were asked for their details several times over. Often where doctors appeared to be doing little ... it was unclear if this was because there was no cure or because they were thought too old to benefit.'

'There were mixed views about the quality of (community health) services' while 'domiciliary (social) services were widely valued for enabling older people to remain in their own homes and seemingly less for being stigmatised than institutional forms of care' (ibid.). Few of the participants had had experience of day centres, after-care, continuing care or nursing homes, but there was much abstract concern and sometimes strongly held views. Overall, while some of the participants expressed almost total satisfaction with the health services, many problems were recognised.

The skills of the primary care physician are especially valued in their ability to distinguish ephemeral complaints from signs of potentially serious disorders. A 'good doctor', among many other skills, has the ability to communicate reassurance convincingly when appropriate and constructive empathy when the news is bad. It is also understood why great importance is attached to prompt referral and access to the investigation, diagnostic and treatment skills of specialist hospital units, and why signs of delay, a blasé manner or poor communication elicit so many complaints It is also understood why an entitlement to domiciliary treatment and support is highly valued, and why to know that community health staff are well trained, accredited and humane is so important. The list could be extended to the domiciliary and residential services. The general point is that older people's consciousness of their human state and vulnerabilities is bound to raise their awareness of the functions of all sectors of health and social care in a way that the young middle-aged person will rarely consider. To the older person, it is of literally vital importance to know that the primary, acute, community health and personal social services, and the mental health and residential and nursing home services, are 'there' and, if and when needed, will be deployed. The prime need is for a well integrated system of services that responds promptly, efficiently and sensitively to each given need. The question that has pervaded this report is whether, given London's size and complexity, that is what we have.

2 The needs of London's older population

A sensible first assumption is that the health and social service needs of older people in London are basically the same as elsewhere in Britain and comparable countries. We have, however, considered some marginal ways in which London's older population is distinctive. The main findings are these: compared with England as a whole, London has a slight under-representation of people aged 60 years and over. If the population estimates are right (about which more below), the under-representation is, however, concentrated in the younger age-groups and the shortfall of those aged 80 years and over in relation to the national age structure is not great. The consequence is that a relatively high share of London's older people are in the oldest age-groups and their average age is slightly higher than in the rest of England. This may be important both in capitation resourcing and in moulding political, managerial and professional attitudes.

Because London has a relatively small share of older people, it does not mean that the task of caring for the individual's health and social service needs is less than elsewhere. Given the positive association between the age of older people and their use of the health and social services, the *per capita* service requirement could be higher. Capitation formulae that weight only for the entire pensionable population would then tend to under-estimate demands on London's health and social services. All sectors of the health and social care services have client profiles that justify capitation formulae which explicitly recognise the number of people in the oldest age-groups, 75–84 and 85 years and over. This is often done, but sometimes the weakness is that the annual estimates of the size of the population are least forthcoming and least reliable for the small service areas in which population change is most rapid. For similar reasons, the community health and personal social services, being most responsible for domiciliary services, have good reason to demand resource allocation weights that reflect the proportion of the oldest residents who live alone.

Another source of distinctiveness is London's migration exchanges. Around one-fifth of London's residents passing through the ages of retirement leave the capital, many moving just beyond the boundary into the Home Counties, others moving to the South West region and to East Anglia. The exodus is socially selective and must reduce the average income and social 'status' of the remaining population. More investigation is required to specify the net effects of the migration exchanges on the socio-economic composition, health status and survival of London's older population. The mass movement is of younger, healthy and active older people, but a minority element is of the most frail and dependent, who leave to live with or near carers and supporters or to enter institutional care. The net result is probably to lower the mean health status of London's older people. Even in Kensington, Christina Victor (1996) observed, 'The older people who remain are among the more deprived, experience above average ill-health and poverty, and have less access to caring resources because of out-migration by younger relatives.'

The effect might be compounded at the oldest ages, because although the shortage of nursing homes in inner London undoubtedly results in moves to homes in outer London and beyond (which would raise the mean health status of the remaining population), it is also likely to result in more of the highly dependent living in their own homes than would be found elsewhere. There is credibility in the claims from primary care and the community health and social services that the average level of need among their older patients and clients has been rising. The substantial migration exchanges mean that even if London's working-age (or adult) population is relatively affluent, well-educated and healthy, it cannot be assumed that the same applies to older people.

Victor's observations describe an outcome that one would expect from the large retirement out-migration but are inconsistent with many population-based measures, such as the relative death rates and the census reports of limiting long-term illness. Some years ago Fox and co-workers (1982, 1985) demonstrated the problem of mismatching numerators and denominators in the calculation of mortality schedules by social class. It is possible that the high mobility of Londoners, the association of a move into a nursing home with an out-migration, and an unusual complement of *pied-à-terres* and second homes, lead to repeated over-estimates of London's population in the oldest age-groups. If so, the inflated denominators would account for some of the more surprising favourable mortality and health indicators for inner-deprived London.

The most distinctive of London's demographic characteristics is the high representation of minority ethnic groups and the diversity and dynamism of these populations. While the absolute and relative number of their older people is presently low, the Black-Caribbean total is growing quickly and, throughout London, will continue to do so for at least two decades. The total of older people of Indian origin will also grow quickly, with greater numbers in outer than inner London. Before two decades have passed, the older population of the Pakistani and Bangladeshi populations will have high rates of increase (although the absolute numbers will be low for many decades to come). London's health and social welfare system has only just begun the required adjustments to provide an effective and equitable service for minority ethnic older people. Most of the present cohorts were born in third-world countries of origin, many in circumstances of absolute poverty, malnutrition and few health services. Their adult lives will in many cases have been marked by arduous manual and domestic labour. Other handicaps among today's minority ethnic elders are that many have little or no command of the English language and a poor knowledge of English health and welfare institutions. Much more could certainly be learnt about the vulnerabilities and predisposition to disease and disorder in the various ethnic populations of London and about the present service response. The sheer diversity of the minorities will require intricate and painstaking data collection.

Some parts of the NHS serve the minority ethnic populations well. Pharoah's (1995) sample of GPs in targeted FHSAs with large minority ethnic populations found among 108 practitioners, that 46 were of Asian origin. The consultation rates of the minority ethnic groups are generally high. It is not known if this generalisation applies to older people *in London*, of whom a large proportion in the Asian-origin communities live with relatives or others of a younger generation. They may have less than usual ability to choose and act independently. London GPs were much more likely than those elsewhere to deny that older people from black and minority ethnic groups had a high consultation rate (op. cit.).

But many aspects of the NHS services are not well adapted to the minority populations and are a cause for concern. There are for example relatively few GPs from the Black-Caribbean, African and Black-British minorities. Non-registration with the NHS among black people is reported as a problem. Low referral rates of older patients to the community health services have been reported (Badger *et al.*, 1989). No evidence has come forward to indicate amelioration in London. The reasons for the low referrals are not fully understood. Among Pharoah's sample of white UK doctors, 34 per cent mentioned the availability of family support, but among Asian-origin doctors, only 18 per cent did so. Instead they pointed to the patients' poor knowledge of services and to language barriers. 'They were twice as likely to mention poor responsiveness and inflexibility in the services as barriers, as well as the lack of health education, low expectations and pride among the patients' (Pharoah, 1995).

There could be a self-reinforcing circle of causation. If a service has not adapted to a culturally distinct and non-English speaking group, it will provide them with few benefits. Neither the patients/clients, nor the professionals who refer, will be encouraged to use the service. That results in no apparent demand from the minority, and no pressure on that service to adapt to the group. The below average utilisation is perceived to be a problem only by the small number who have need of the service, do not receive it, but know that they should. Ethnic monitoring of hospital in-patient and out-patient and community health service contacts has not yet fed through to the standard, central statistical series, so there is little knowledge of the comparative utilisation of hospital services by minority ethnic older people.

There are many reasons for more vigorous attention to the health and health service needs of minority ethnic older people in London. Each DHA might do more to produce health and needs profiles of the various ethnic groups and to audit local services. A greater advance would be if standard information was collected for the entire city. Patterns of treatment and referral should be critically examined, and the least justifiable irregularities addressed directly. There is a case for more widespread and targeted training of NHS staff in many sectors of the service, to increase their knowledge of the contrasting social, cultural and material biographies and living conditions of the current older population. One challenge will be to design effective training syllabuses, for there are so many minority ethnic groups and so many languages, religions and 'value-systems', that it is clearly unreasonable to expect all health and social welfare professionals to be informed in depth about all groups. That problem will in turn stimulate advocacy for segregated services, perhaps particularly in the residential and nursing home sectors, all of which will test the managerial and community relations policies and skills of the providers.

3 Population projections: more or fewer older people in London?

London's population in advanced old age (85 years and over) increased very rapidly during the first half of the 1990s, by just under a quarter for men. This was probably an echo of events 80 years ago. Men aged 85–90 years in 1993 were born in 1903–8 and were just too young to fight in the First World War. They were not therefore depleted by the heavy losses of the Great War campaigns and, in comparison to those born five and ten years before, many more have survived to their 80s. The anticipated increase of the population of 85 years and over in the later 1990s is much lower and, for at least a decade from the end of the century, projections suggest that the general pattern will be for decreases of London's older population in all age-groups. The next strong surge of London's older population will probably not come until the 2030s. Alarmism in London's health and social services about the impacts of a 'demographic time bomb' is quite misplaced.

4 Primary care and older people in London

There have been substantial investments and changes in general practice throughout the United Kingdom during the 1990s and, through special funding, more in London than elsewhere. Extended surgery hours and improved appointments arrangements are among the welcome signs of heightened attention to the 'customer interest'. Considerable investments from both NHS funds and partnership capital have raised the quality of the consulting and waiting rooms and diversified the facilities of health centres. Special to London, Tomlinson or London Initiative Funds have supported many improvements in premises and in support staff although, for the latter at least, the cessation of fixed-term funds has seen many withdraw. Several DHAs and locality purchasing groups have taken initiatives around the 75 years and over health check and are now planning primary care services for older people, as the agencies' annual reports and purchasing plans testify. It is not clear, however, whether the number of GPs in London has increased during the 1990s, nor whether they are providing as many or more consultations and contacts *per capita* as at the beginning of the decade. It remains the case that a low proportion of London GPs are fundholders and that a high proportion work in single-handed practices. The overall impression is that although London is not markedly under-doctored, the services that their practices provide still do not attain the national standard.

It appears unavoidable that more and more support will be required for general practice in London (and elsewhere) to give the service the capacity not only to meet rising demands, but also to play a part in reversing this country's declining position in the older persons' health league of European nations. As ever, superficially it appears that pro-active approaches, including screening and health promotion work, would be effective. But hard evidence in support is limited and countered by legitimate objections. Screening may not be the best use of the scarce time of physicians or practice staff. The surgery or health centre may not be the best medium or location for health promotion. But it is dismaying to read so many accounts of the marginalisation of the 75 years and over annual health check, and to find so little enthusiasm for making it more efficient and effective.

No information has come to hand about whether London's older people regard the GP service as having improved, deteriorated or remained much the same during the 1990s. It may be that positive attitudes are widespread: we simply do not know. If in the health and social welfare services as in other spheres of life, problems and deficiencies attract far more attention than things that are working well, then those who support the founding principles of the NHS, as well as advocates for the recent and anticipated primary care reforms, would be well advised to bring together a coherent and well-grounded evaluation of change in the sector and, particularly, a rigorously representative account of the patients' views. There would be positive benefits to older people if their widespread concerns about hospital closures and long-term care were allayed by a clear perception of the strengths of the NHS and the improvements that are achieved.

5 Hospital services for London's older people

A careful examination of purchasing and providing data, including contact rates and finished consultant episode (FCE) rates, shows that although NHS expenditure is markedly higher *per capita* in London than in the remainder of England, the differential is substantially lessened when (a) the teaching and research functions of London hospitals are removed, and (b) the provision of treatment and care to non-Londoners is discounted. Examination of the number and rate of FCEs for patients allocated to their home addresses makes this possible. London's hospitals in 1994–95 provided 1.44 million FCEs, 15.4 per cent of the total in England, a little above London's 14 per cent share of England's population. Residents of the capital received 1.28 million episodes, 1.24 million from London hospitals and 37,000 from hospitals outside the capital. Londoners therefore received 13.7 per cent of all FCEs in England, slightly *less* (0.96) than their 14.3 per cent share of the population (Boyle and Hamblin, 1997).

Partly reflecting the age structure of London's resident population, but inevitably reflecting also the ages of its many non-resident workers and visitors, the delivered FCEs are biased towards the working ages. The age-sex *standardised* hospitalisation rate for London DHAs is approximately three FCEs per 1,000 less than in England (Boyle and Hamblin, 1997). When services to the older population are specifically examined, the 1994–95 FCE rate per head in London virtually matches that for the rest of England. There was slightly high provision to the youngest older females, particularly by providers in the inner-deprived and intermediate mixed-status zones, but a markedly low rate of provision to females aged 85 years and over, particularly by providers in the intermediate, mixed-status and outer, high-status zones.

The FCE rates for older people (from any area of residence) by specialty do show some marked differentials between London and the rest of the country and among the three zones of London. General medicine FCE provision is exceptionally high in inner London. Several other specialties returned national or slightly below national rates, with a tendency for under-provision to be most widespread among outer London providers. The most consistent under-provision was for the psychiatric FCEs. Geriatric specialty FCEs are generally below national rates of provision in London, and particularly so for those aged less than 75 years by the providers in the outer, high-status districts.

Returning to the FCEs provided to London's *resident* older population, certain diagnoses return remarkably low rates of hospitalisation for the inner-deprived zones. This is an important cautionary finding, for the above average aggregate expenditure on London's hospitals and the relatively favourable rates of all-age provision disguise the existence of a problem. The directorates of the inner London health authorities do not see the issue. Having commissioned from the Department of Health an analysis of the beds used by Londoners rather than available beds, they concluded that 'while on a crude population basis Londoners use fewer beds than the England average, residents of inner London use 17 per cent more beds than would be expected given the structure of the population ... elderly Londoners are disproportionately high users of the health services, probably because of poor access to domiciliary care and nursing homes' (Department of Health, 1995). On three out of four counts, this assessment is the inverse of that reached in this report.

Misinterpretations of the *per capita* utilisation of services by *resident* older people in inner (and outer) London wittingly or unconsciously may be used to justify further retrenchment of London's hospital beds, and the consequence could well be that London's older people quickly acquire substantially below national rates of treatment. This would be the most likely result if the specialist units with a regional or national function are protected to a greater extent than the general medicine, surgical and orthopaedic beds that provide for the majority of episodes. There may be a strong case for not just the protection but the expansion of psychogeriatric and 'care of the elderly' provision. There is also an urgent need to identify the reasons for the very low rates of hospitalisation in several specialties to the local population in the inner areas. Is it mainly a consequence of the characteristics of London hospital provision, or is it mainly a consequence of weaknesses in London's general medical practice – which is failing to make adequate referrals to the hospitals?

Here is the first of several issues about the inter-sectoral or system level performance of London's health and social services that, from the limited available evidence, appear defective and are causes for concern. These aspects of service delivery and effectiveness should be monitored but no one authority currently has that responsibility. The merits of establishing a unit to collate the system's operational statistics and population-based performance measures for London as a whole, and which is charged particularly to monitor the adequacy of the services delivered to the inner areas deserves further consideration.

6 Community health services for London's older people

The community health services for older people principally serve disabled, vulnerable and convalescent patients. Their main client groups are peri-natal women, young infants, the physically disabled, those recovering from serious traumas and operations, and chronically and multiply sick, frail older people. There is often no clear line which separates the community health service patient from the client of the personal social services. Further complicating their work with their older patients, virtually all are under the active care of general practitioners, and many have regimens of treatment designed by hospital consultants.

The community and mental health service NHS trusts in London in 1994–95 received 19.2 per cent of the expenditure in England but provided only 13.8 per cent of the community service contacts. When broken down by the major services for older clients, London's population received approximately national rates of service from district nurses, health visitors and (statutory provider) chiropodists, but substantially above average contact rates from speech therapists and dieticians. The standard reporting series do not permit analyses of community health service provision by the age of the patients or clients. Even if they did, it would be far from easy to evaluate the outputs and effectiveness of the community health services from the operational data (most of which is collected for workload planning and remuneration purposes) (Warnes et al., 1995). The hours, urgency, intensity and impact of the therapeutic treatments, nursing care and instrumental support offered by their staff vary immensely, and the variations are unlikely to be represented adequately in patient-rates or contact hours. Much better outcome measures are in principle possible for some services, notably occupational and speech therapy, but episodes are long. Useful comparative measures require very careful definition and should be centrally collected.

Individual community trusts collect enhanced reports of their provision, from which a high concentration of services on patients aged 75 years and over is apparent (Koffman, 1997). One day's survey in February 1997 of district nurse activity in Riverside Community Health Care NHS Trust, which serves Kensington, Chelsea and Westminster, showed that 87.6 per cent of 899 contacts were with patients aged 65 years and over, and that nearly 40 per cent of all contacts were with patients aged 85 years and over (a 10 percentage points increase on 1996). Similar reports from Wandsworth Community Health Care NHS Trust have been received.

One perception within the community health services is that their workload from older patients has increased substantially in recent years because of deficiencies in the other health and social care sectors. It may be, however, that the rapid increase in the population aged 85 years and over during the early 1990s (explained above) has been the main factor. Crude resource allocation formulae would neither have anticipated nor provided the means to deal with this increase, again pointing to the poor information environment in which the sector is working. A key requirement for the community health services in London as elsewhere is that more detailed information about their operations, patients and outputs is centrally available. In particular, the ages and ethnic group membership of the patients and clients must be available to enable the evaluation of the services delivered to older people in different communities.

The community health services have an 'image problem' among the general public, politicians and other health professionals. They have neither the impressive physical plant or the association with critical care that acute hospitals enjoy, nor the universality of general medical practice. They serve by comparison only a small minority of the population. Among older people, however, their importance is rated highly. The treatments and therapies they provide materially raise the quality of life of their patients. The concern and attention shown demonstrably raises patients' self-esteem and morale (Neuberger, 1993).

For several of the community health services, setting the outcomes of treatment and care and measuring the effectiveness of their delivery is problematic. This is partly because the benefits are in the patients' physical, mental and social states and, as well as being highly individualised responses, all are often confounded by parallel conditions and relapse and unrelated events. Another reason is that the many therapeutic courses have long or variable durations, as with recovery from stroke. A third is that the progress of a patient is a function not only of the quality of the community health services, but also of general practice and hospital-based care and of family support. The CHS evidently must work closely with the other health sectors and the personal social services. There is plenty of evidence that the best in London do. Innumerable joint working arrangements are found, and many clearly operate with impressive vigour, common sense and fortitude. If there is a problem, it is that so much depends on the energy and personalities of each constellation of providers. As sociologists might say, and as found widely in the public services, much depends on charisma and the elusive chemistry of inter-professional working.

What is missing is once again the responsible body and the procedures for monitoring performance and to provide, when appropriate, the support or the sanctions to strengthen poor service. At present it is difficult to compile other than the most superficial overview of the quality and outcomes of community health services. Even routinely collected operational data are reported unevenly and are seriously deficient – with, for example, the ages of patients on the outcomes of treatment episodes largely hidden from us. The sector-specific operational data are, however, an inadequate basis for evaluating the contribution of the community health services to raising the health and well-being of older people. The only way to assess the quality of the health and social services delivered to disabled or chronically and multiply sick older people (or others) is to assess them 'in the round' and from the vantage point of the patient.

The district health authorities could be more pro-active in promoting co-ordination among the 'older people services'. The community care plans should include more information on the socio-demographic, health and needs profiles of the older population. Such exercises have of course sometimes accompanied local experiments and *ad hoc* working arrangements. The need is for a wider and standing monitoring and evaluation process. The design of the data collection, storage and routine reporting would be a demanding exercise. It may not be possible to incorporate the required recording tasks in the job descriptions of the front-line staff, and dedicated surveys are expensive. But however it is done, system-wide appraisal information is a necessary condition before an over-arching body can intervene to raise the quality and effectiveness of multi-sector care.

The insistent cause of concern which is prompted by the massive variations in the provision of community health services across London and by abstract inferences about the implications for older patients of the administrative balkanisation of the NHS and statutory social care is that there is much neglect. The case for a system level responsible body is especially strong when there are many providing 'cells'. Among the public health functions which could usefully be charged to a London-wide body, a special responsibility to monitor the quality of all care received by chronically sick and disabled older people living in the community would be an exciting innovation of great value. Individual health authorities are not charged with responsibility for this kind of analysis for London as a whole and spend limited time on the task within their own areas. Their pre-occupation with acute services issues has left this area of work seriously neglected.

7 Social services and community care

Chronically and multiply unwell and socially isolated older people are the principal clients of the community health and personal social services dedicated to older people. A combination of historical, professional and political considerations have brought about their separated management, the health services through independent trusts, the latter through local government. The designated 'elderly' services are the prime setting for physicians' and social workers' assessments of needs. 'care of the elderly' physicians are concerned with medical, after-care and continuing-care needs: for the latter, they turn to community health services, independent nursing homes, informal carers or the social services. Social workers are concerned with the non-medical needs of elderly people for nursing care and instrumental support.

These complexities and the great cost of continuing-care have produced intense policy and ethical debates in all developed countries. The debate is coloured by emotions and principles with moral, humanitarian and even egocentric roots – in political ideologies, class and religious prejudices and the personal fear of ageing and death. London's political geography differs from that of other major English cities only in degree. Most of the inner boroughs are 'solid Labour' with a strong commitment to social services, reinforced in several by heightened awareness of the disadvantage and discrimination experienced by members of their large minority ethnic populations. Special to London are the high status, Conservative inner boroughs, especially in the West End, with affluent populations.

The most recent attempt to increase the health and social care benefits of spending in this field arose from Sir Roy Griffiths's (1988) review of the system and his recommendations in *Community Care: Agenda for Action* (Department of Health, 1989, 1990). The aim was to devise a rational system for assessing an individual's needs and designing and purchasing 'care packages'. With some delay, these were implemented in the 1993 community care provisions of the 1990 National Health Service Act. Local authority social service departments were given the prime role of assessment and care planning, but the role of local authorities as direct providers (of residential and domiciliary care) was to be curtailed.

The implementation of the 'community care provisions' has not been smooth. A host of problems has intervened, including inadequate capital and recurrent funding; party political resistance (mainly to the cutting of direct provision in inner city areas); professional boundaries, inertia and resistance in both medical and social work areas; and the simultaneous changes in the NHS which have cut continuing or long-term care beds, and pressured hospital managers to reduce the duration of hospital episodes and to discharge those for whom no further 'medical need' can be determined. Technical difficulties included legal concerns on the part of Social Service departments about detailing unmet need in their community care plans, prompting a letter from the Social Services Directorate to the London SSD directors that 'unmet choice' might be recorded in its stead (Department of Health, 1993).

Many evaluations of the implementation of the community care provisions are now appearing, including several for London, but the overall picture remains confused (Lewis and Glennerster, 1996; Wistow and Hardy, 1994). Howse and Dalley's (1996) substantial review, commissioned for this study, concludes that 'shortages of resources in local authority social services departments do seem to be having a knock-on effect for the health service. Where there are problems of delayed discharges, it seems to be caused by a mix of factors: in some cases it may be the failure of the SSDs to provide the funding for necessary packages of care, in others by a lack of residential places. In certain cases, delays are caused while people's houses are sold to free resources. There was little evidence of delays being caused by difficulties internal to the health service. This means in many instances, that the satisfactory discharge of NHS responsibility to meet the needs of older people is compromised' (op. cit.). The position adopted by individual health authorities in relation to continuing-care varies. Some seek to increase NHS provision, others to reduce it drastically, and others intend to maintain the *status quo*. There is a trend to place patients with continuing-care needs in the independent sector, which is being co-opted as an arm of the health service with little public debate, little planning and little discussion within the sector itself at any strategic level.

With hindsight, to implement strategic change without addressing explicitly the complementary roles of the health and social services, and of acute trusts, community trusts, and the social service departments, and without setting a clear financial framework, was to perpetuate muddle, making-do and sectoral conflict. The election of a fresh government and the intention to establish a London-wide elected body provides an excellent opportunity for a more carefully designed implementation of community care. The final chapter elaborates the possibilities and makes specific recommendations. But first, a summary is provided of the main causes for concern about health and social services for older people in London.

8 Sector-specific weaknesses of the health and social services for older people in London

This review of the health and social services provided to London's older people suggests the following deficiencies and causes for concern. Most can be described but not incontrovertibly explained given existing information sources.

Hospitalisation rates in inner London

The lead issue is why there is such a low rate of hospitalisation for London's inner area resident older people and why this has not previously been proclaimed as a serious weakness. The fact may have been disguised by the more favourable performance indicators for the entire city and for all age-groups, but the under-provision has not been heavily camouflaged. Is it primarily a consequence of the historical development and prestigious characteristics of the hospitals, or is it mainly caused by a low rate of GP consultations? The central London hospitals are well provided with 'medicine' beds but are poorly provided with 'care of the elderly' beds. Is the relative absence in inner London of 'care of the elderly' physicians, who are trained to assess the needs of patients with multiple and chronic disorders prior to referral to the organ-based specialties, demonstrated by the low FCE rates? Or is the source of the problem less specific, a consequence of the importance in the major acute trusts of specialist treatments, training, research and private practice? A further possibility is that at least part of the low hospitalisation rate be explained by the dearth of nursing homes in inner London. Do so many of the most frail and dependent of inner London's older people move to nursing homes in outer London or beyond, that a significant redistribution occurs in the hospital admissions for the group's sequelae events.

General practice in inner London

If there is a low rate of GP consultation with the older population in London, or if the proportion of the 75 years and over health checks that are conducted by GPs themselves is low, then *ceteris paribus* the rate of referral to hospital consultants would also be low. It might also be true that the rates of consultations both during the course of, and following, each hospital episode are low; and that referrals from GPs to the community health services are below the national level. Another theoretical possibility is that when there is a low rate of consultations with the general practice services, the average severity of the presenting conditions rises. Put another way, a smaller proportion of presentations (and therefore diagnoses) are 'early', and a higher proportion are 'late'. For several common critical events, that would result in a smaller proportion of the age-group being admitted to hospital early in their progression, and a high proportion of the episodes concluding with hospital deaths. Such a differential was indeed found between London and comparable areas in the rest of England for patients aged 85 years and over. As a similar differential was not found for the younger elderly age-groups (where the effect would be most likely to show), the chain of reasoning is not proved, but one wonders what distortions arise from the high percentage of non-resident elderly patients treated by the London hospitals. Could the 'import' of patients aged 65–84 years from long distances select for those with a high chance of recovery and home discharge? If so, they would mask a high percentage of deaths among London resident patients. The hypotheses deserve further investigation, which would only begin with the hospital discharge pattern for London residents. The key information is about the referral rates and destinations by GPs to other health and social services. The required database would however be of extraordinary complexity and size. The national Morbidity Statistics from General Practice do not collect such data (McCormack *et al.*, 1995).

The main points of the review of general practitioners and general practice services in *The Health Economy of London* are that the capital still has an unusually high percentage of practices in sub-standard premises, that London GPs perform badly against several performance targets (although the completion of the 75 years and over health check was not included), that the average age of London GPs remains high, and that the employment of practice support staff remains low. There has however been improvement on several measures since the early 1990s, some undoubtedly associated with the London Initiative Zone funds. The improvements in practice premises are clearly durable, but some of the staffing and service gains may be ephemeral. At the present time, few comparative judgements can be made about GP services to the London's older residents, and the possibility remains that they are markedly deficient.

The variability of community health care services

The limited evidence which is available and which has been examined suggests that although London overall has approximately average rates of community health service provision, there is unusual variability among the trusts and little of this has an apparent basis in need. It should be emphasised again, however, that the information sources are particularly fragmented and weak for this service. The case for a London wide health statistics collection and maintenance service is no more pressing than for this sector. Currently the available data are mainly crude operational variables, and most analyses are insensitive to the size and change in the oldest age-groups. It makes little sense to express community health contacts *per capita* of the entire population when the services are so polarised as between child and very old patients.

The other clear feature of London's community health services is their high cost, which is readily explained by salary, wage, recruitment, training, premises, and transport costs. A considerable element of the high costs is also attributable to the pattern of service delivery and the dependency status of London patients. Several sources suggest that the community health services in London are supporting patients that are more dependent than in the rest of the country, and that therefore they deliver more hours of care and support to relatively fewer patients. If this is the case, an explanation would be illuminating. Is it a by-product of the low hospitalisation rate for London residents, the under-provision of nursing homes, or of attenuated family support networks among London's older people?

Mental health services for older people

As the report on *London's Mental Health* for the Commission demonstrated (Johnson *et al.*, 1997), and as the analyses of hospital utilisation confirm, mental health services and particularly psychogeriatric beds for older people are both under-developed and very unevenly available across London. The low ratio of general practice support staff and the relatively high average of GPs would also suggest a below average response to affective mental ill-health.

Residential and nursing home capacity

A long-established feature of London has been the dearth of private sector residential and nursing home care in inner London and its relative concentration in the outer suburbs. Until the 1990s, this pattern was compensated by a high rate of local authority residential care provision in the inner boroughs, and high rates of provision of the domiciliary personal social services. These latter services are now severely challenged by the aims of the 1993 community care reforms which are being enforced by funding changes. The reforms particularly disadvantage the poorest older people living in London. The character of the inner London boroughs, and of their residential property values, suggest that without specific interventions the area's relatively low provision of private sector residential care will never be corrected.

A prime cause of low residential and nursing home provision in London and particularly the inner areas is land and property values. The NHS does, however, have an extensive estate in all parts of London. While each trust and the Treasury have good reason to maximise the yield from unused premises and land, disposals have been restrained and there are many vacant and under-utilised former hospital sites. Here is an opportunity to revitalise the Private Finance Initiative in a socially productive way. How much easier it would be to gain consent for a ward or hospital closure if at the same time it was announced that the premises were to be converted to some form of nursing or continuing-care home.

9 Immediate tasks for further investigation and action

Action to tackle these problems clearly lies, in some cases, with individual sectors and providers, but most require further investigation and then will need collaborative action across more than one sector. The most urgent tasks are believed to be to:

- investigate and account for the low rate of hospital provision to older people in the inner-deprived areas;
- evaluate the impact of the changes in London's general medical practice services on the services provided to older patients;
- bring London's mental health services for older people up to national levels of provision, and reduce variations within London;
- prepare all sectors of London's health and social services for rapid growth in the population of minority ethnic older people;

- decompose the variations in community health service provision for older patients across London into the elements that are matters of nomenclature, that reflect variations in need and the residue, and audit both the health care benefits and gains and the cost-effectiveness of the variable provision.

As evaluations of specific services are pursued, two realisations are common: first that the information to reach a conclusion has still to be collected or analysed, and second that many of the important issues cannot be understood by examining each service sector in isolation but rather are matters of their contribution to a wider pattern of care. The effectiveness of their collaboration and liaison with other sectors is especially important for the older patient or client. It is to these issues that the final chapter turns.

Chapter 6

A system prospectus

Summary

- Unconscious age stereotyping continues to handicap the vigorous development of services for older people. Few see the 'care of the elderly' services as having clinical or professional prestige. A strong 'community medicine and well-being' perspective on service priorities will change this state.

- A simplistic understanding is widely held of the chronicity and irreversibility of many of the degenerative and progressive disorders found among the most impaired older people. It pervades and distorts many representations of the overall health care needs of the older population. For the majority, treatment can improve health and functioning, and recovery from episodes of ill-health is normal.

- An integrated understanding is required, that incorporates knowledge of the relative prevalence and age distributions of needs for primary care, of needs for the treatment of acute episodes including after-care, and of the chronically sick and disabled patients' needs for intensive and continuing treatment and domiciliary or nursing-home care.

- Of all groups of patients, those with degenerative, multiple and chronic conditions are most likely to lose out. Their conditions require continuing or lengthy episodes of treatment, often from several providers, and often with complex interacting effects. Older people predominate in the group. The majority are relatively young and their health and functioning improves when well managed regimens are applied.

- No single regional body has had strategic responsibility for the capital's health services, and no London-wide body has had responsibility to overview the implementation of community care by the borough social services departments.

- The configuration of purchasers and providers established in the NHS internal market is ill-designed to place a high priority on inter-agency and inter-sector care. Providing agencies have a perverse incentive to reduce their contribution to multi-agency packages of care.

- The effect is compounded by the division of responsibility for the health services and the social services (even at the level of Departments of State). Two funding streams for the provision of integrated health and social care result, producing two ways in which other claims divert resources.

- Health authorities as commissioners can promote the patient interest and act as 'referees' if only among health providers but their attention focuses on acute hospitals and their staffing is being reduced. The extension of primary care commissioning is not necessarily incompatible with the retention of district level purchasing objectives but raises many organisational difficulties, concerning particularly funding streams.

- Social services for older people developed strongly during the 1980s but financial cuts during the last few years have compromised their continued improvement. The inception of 'care assessment' may have concentrated care to those with the highest levels of need.

- There is lamentably little patient- and population-based monitoring and evaluation of the services provided to the older population. A rigorously designed 'customer-based' standing inquiry across all health and social services should be established to enable regular and penetrating audits of inter-sectoral service delivery and patient or client outcomes.

- There are many examples in London of willingness and enthusiasm to establish joint working and funding arrangements for older people's services. They demonstrate a widespread acknowledgement among providers that the existing structures and procedures for providing treatment and care to the most dependent older people are inadequate. Fewer schemes tackle the problems of managing protracted acute episodes involving several providers.

- Local initiatives in joint commissioning and provision depend on goodwill and *ultra vires* effort. They are laudatory and valuable experiments but inadequate to the necessary task of establishing mandatory, system-wide mechanisms for the monitoring of inter-agency and inter-sectoral treatment and care.

- The first step in bringing about 'seamless' care for older people, which is close to present practice in some areas of London, is for community health care NHS trusts and borough social service departments' budgets for 'older people services' to be unequivocally itemised and pooled for defined common populations. Joint or multi-agency management of all statutory domiciliary and day care services for older people should be established.

- The further challenge is to establish effective mechanisms for monitoring, evaluating and managing the complex treatment pathways of acute episodes as well as the treatment and care of those with high requirements for health and social care. The medium-term goal should be to establish not only the effective audit of multi-provider and inter-sectoral care but also effective powers and mechanisms to correct sub-optimal treatment and care 'routing' and outcomes.

> • One option would be to create a London-wide auditing and regulatory body with a judicious combination of rights to be heard and to persuade. This body would have reserve financial powers to effect change in the configuration of health *and* social services. Its implementation could be phased, not by sectors of care, but by the groups of patients it is charged to overview.

1 Evaluating London's health and social services for older people

This final chapter focuses on the systemic aspects of London's health and social services. It is particularly concerned with issues of co-operation, co-ordination and communication. The importance of these functions in the delivery of services to older people is reiterated, and some reasons for the slight attention given to them in the organisation and management of the statutory services are explored. The absence of inter-agency and inter-sectoral operational data is highlighted. The weaknesses and problems of 'older people' care have come to a head in the implementation of the community care provisions of the NHS and Community Care Act 1990. The report concludes with suggestions for the steps that need to be taken not only to improve the equity and effectiveness of 'care-management' but also to extend more widely the functions of patient-oriented monitoring and system-level management.

The test that is applied here to London's health and social is the appropriateness and quality of services delivered to older people. This report has examined many topics and diverse health and social services. The common thread is the inter-relationships between four sets of characteristics:

- of older people and their heterogeneous illnesses, acute episodes, frailty and dependency;
- of the health and social services that they need given their health and social status,
- of London's health and social care system, together with some special factors in its use that arise from the great size and complexity of the city;
- of the services that older patients and clients actually receive.

With all these described, however incompletely, it is possible to formulate several kinds of conclusion about the current system of services and care. Most of the evidence is about the relative availability and output of individual services, as was the focus of the previous chapter. Some services, such as psychogeriatric beds, have been found to be indisputably under-provided throughout London by comparison with the rest of the country or other cities. Others have outstandingly uneven provision. Some, as with acute hospital episodes, independent nursing homes and general dental practitioners, vary along an inner-area to outer-area dimension. Others, as with specific community health services and 'care-managed packages', change more haphazardly by health district, borough or neighbourhood. One can also identify services which although having national and relatively invariable rates of provision are exceptionally expensive, such as several of the major community health and personal social services. The effect will be to divert resources from other forms of care. Their high costs are *prima-facie* evidence of sub-optimal effectiveness in the system.

The appraisal of individual services is however a poor tool for assessing the quality and effectiveness of health and social services for older people, who know better than others that the quality of a national health and social care service depends crucially on the continuity of treatment and care, even when this involves more than one physician (or professional) and more than one providing agency. They also know that some deficiencies in such continuity are inevitable, but that many which presently occur could be avoided. One day a person can manage at home independently, the next they cannot; one week another manages at home with social service support, the next they need the care and support of a nursing home. That said, avoidable lapses in the quality of care as a result of poor communication and liaison are frequently remarked upon by patients and many well informed staff of the NHS. By their nature, they are impossible to quantify from operational data, and in the absence of market or patient-based surveys from any source, their extent and nature remains largely unknown.

2 The marginalisation of the older patient and client

One possible explanation for the scarcity of information on older people's health and the use of the health services is a familiar lament, that many health service professionals find older people's health and care needs unexciting and lacking scientific or clinical prestige. Such attitudes have several deep-seated roots. One common 'taken for granted' belief is that to prolong a young life is a superior act to the prolongation of an old life. A few have reached the position philosophically on material and ethical criteria: debates on this issue raise fundamental questions about the value of human lives (Moody, 1988, 1995). Daniel Callahan, the American health care ethicist, has for some years recommended the withdrawal of high-technology therapies from those who exceed their 'natural span' (Callahan, 1987, 1990). There are however a host of mundane reasons why the health and well-being of 'old', 'unproductive' and 'incurable' patients and clients do not inspire noviciate professionals and weary the experienced. Only a gifted few come to see that the chronicity and irreversibility of many disorders in later life make diagnosis, prognosis and treatment planning for older patients an exceptionally demanding branch of practice.

The tendency to equate older people's health care needs with those of the frailest and most dependent minority itself marginalises the task. As Charles Freer saw, 'It is likely that when asked to think of an old person, most of us, whether lay or professional, are likely to picture a frail, bent person, slow to move and think and short of memory. More specific medical stereotypes, such as incontinence, dementia and deafness are also likely to spring to mind' (Freer, 1988). He added, 'A particular illustration of ageism is in the context of community and primary care of the elderly, where many, providers and patients alike, hold a prevailing negative view about the health status of older people and the likely implications of a growing elderly population on the use of services.' Age stereotypes are pervasive in society and are frequently expressed by older people, and ageism remains an insidious deterrent to building positive approaches to services for older people (Bytheway, 1995).

The enduring Cinderella status of 'care of the elderly' services has been driven home during the 1990s by the introduction of the internal market and several of its accompanying managerial practices (Health Advisory Service, 1997). Some of the provider-specific performance indicators, notably those designed to raise the productivity of beds and staff, and the pervasive assertion in medical care settings of the 'effectiveness' criterion, have heightened the importance of medical prognoses in the allocation of NHS care. Put crudely, the asserted principle is that if a patient cannot benefit from medical treatment or nursing care, they should not be NHS patients and certainly not in an acute hospital. Similarly, if a social services client can manage at home and has a carer available (however reluctant), they are not eligible for statutory personal social services.

Several benefits and several problems have flowed from these utilitarian principles. Older people like others are benefiting from the increased number of elective treatments, as with cancer therapy, hip replacement and ophthalmic surgery. They may also be benefiting from the increased resources and more diverse services in general practice. When care and treatment is sector- or specialty-specific, then the organisation of the internal market and the performance indicators that have to date been introduced may indeed work for the patient. But when a patient's needs are more complex and extended, then the new arrangements could well be causing more harm than good. Detailed evidence for this assertion and a weighty expression of the opinion published during the preparation of this report are returned to below.

Turning to the social services for older people, Olive Stevenson, a leading commentator, believes that there has been some progress in raising the age-group's esteem. 'We have moved a long way from the "taken-for-granted" ageist assumptions of the 1960s and 1970s in social services teams, where very little social work was for older people and attitudes expressed towards them were frequently patronising' (Stevenson, 1996).

She adds that the principles advanced in the community care planning and policy implementation documents were encouraging, as with 'the rationale for this re-organisation is the empowerment of users and carers' (Social Services Inspectorate, 1991). 'Raised awareness of the position (and the predicament) of many older people, especially women, and an assertion of the ideal of empowerment for all users combined to offer a real opportunity to make progress in offering more sensitive and imaginative services than before' (Stevenson, 1996).

The bad news, however, is principally the shortage of resources but also procedural heavy-handedness and the persistence of demeaning attitudes. 'Severe resource shortages make a mockery of the ideal of choice in the key process of care management ... or in decisions concerning admission to residential care. ... It is no exaggeration to say that the next few years will decide the credibility of the policy which offered in theory a real opportunity for the empowerment of older people' (ibid.). On demeaning attitudes, Stevenson observes that because 'old people are overwhelmingly the dominant group requiring support in the community and residential care', they tend to be regarded as 'not special' and do not stimulate the energetic advocacy found, for example, for young people with learning disabilities. 'A spotlight is thrown on other community care users whilst very old people are left in the shade. We still hear of unqualified workers "taking on the elderly".'

3 Impediments to the continuity of treatment and care in an internal market

Elementary classical economic theory teaches that in a perfect market there are innumerable adjustment and equilibrating mechanisms that, for example, discipline a provider with high costs, stimulate the supply of services which are in increasing demand, and encourage consumers to substitute low for high-priced goods. Few of these mechanisms apply to a mature 'internal market' of health and social care let alone to one, as now found in the NHS, that is newly-established. Today's 'internal market' still battles to be fully accepted by all those that work in it and by the professional and governmental bodies that control it.

Even in a fully functioning 'internal market', health and social service consumers would still be largely ignorant of the benefits of the care that they wish to purchase (or, more precisely, of the care they wish qualified others to purchase on their behalf). There can never be many opportunities for substituting one treatment or care commodity for another, although different manufacturers' drugs are a notable exception to the rule. Extensive and powerful regulation of the competence and credentials of the staff will ever be required. There will always have to be large cross-subsidies between the services that are more 'profitable' and those, epitomised by emergency and disaster response services, that society deems imperative but are rarely used and very expensive. There would always have to be mechanisms that divert resources from current consumers to support prevention and public health functions for which no individual customer would pay.

It should be emphasised more frequently and loudly how different a 'health care market' is from a 'perfect' or 'free' market. In the NHS internal market *at any one time*, most providers, including community health care trusts, general practices, and specialist acute units, have a market status closer to a monopoly than a competing provider. Only when contracts come up for renewal, or in the few circumstances when one purchaser has a choice of providers for referral to more specialist care (for example a surgical unit or a nursing home), does any resemblance to the regulatory role of price apply. Even then, most services have been organised to provide services to all those in need within a defined district. One can envisage general medical practice going the way of general dental practice and losing this territorial organisation and this being more possible in the high-density environment of London than elsewhere – dentists are now often selected by personal recommendation or for proximity to the place of work rather than to home. Most district hospital, community health and statutory social services will however always be most efficient with spatially defined catchments.

Instead of a 'perfect market', the NHS today is a multiplicity of providers that are care-sector-specific cost-centres. They are not autonomous, least of all financially, and they have to work within a multitude of regulations and restrictions: about the credentials of their employees, about the minimum levels of service they must supply, about levels of productivity, about the financial return from their turn-over and assets, and about a host of ethical precepts. As Anthony Harrison (1997) has reminded us, the performance criteria and accounting disciplines which have been created around NHS trusts tend to encourage an inward looking and organisationally bounded approach to care delivery and overall performance. Some disappointing instances of narrow-minded 'off-loading' can be found in London. More generally and importantly, the agencies and mechanisms for evaluating the performance of the health and social care system *as a whole* have been weakened by the recent policy and organisational reforms. During the Conservative administrations, few advantages of strong centrally-planned public service were believed to exist, and the tendency was to promote flexibility and local autonomy, sometimes by citing the desirable commodity of patient or consumer choice. The emphasis was on mechanisms for the control of aggregate spending and to encourage secondary features of a health and social care system, such as the participation of the independent sector in domiciliary and residential care. A commitment to the measurement of outcomes manifested principally in crude provider-specific performance indicators and sector-specific league tables. These are far from effective tools for the required system evaluation.

The planning and regulatory functions of a top-down, paternalist public service have been weakened, but the system is still a long way from being driven by well-informed, managerially competent consortia of primary care or general practice purchasers who act (in the manner of lawyers) on behalf of their patients. Health authorities turn to their public health departments for indicators of the state of the public's health. Macro-indicators, such as standardised mortality ratios and infant mortality rates are the stock in trade of these exercises, but not only do they rarely examine specifically the survival and health of older people, very often the analyses and measures explicitly *exclude* them. One reason for this is that many variations in health, including those associated with 'deprivation', which are of great concern at the present, have greater amplitude in the working-age than the older population. Public health analysts are tempted away from examining the changing health of older people.

4 Monitoring treatment and care pathways of older patients

The relevance of the points made above is that the recently created 'internal market' requires but does not have effective mechanisms to monitor its overall performance *from the customer perspective.* The customers of J. Sainsbury plc can vote with their feet and their loyalty cards, but this option is not available to NHS patients except for the minority of the privately-insured. Arguably the only proxies for the disciplines of the market are general elections, the take-up of private medical insurance, and the capricious pressures of public opinion as filtered and constructed by the media, elected representatives, and special-interest pressure groups.

It has been stressed that the older population is heterogeneous and that it is a lazy and inaccurate generalisation to describe their health service needs by those of the frailest and oldest minority. The residents of nursing homes and the patients of 'care of the elderly' specialists are a small and atypical minority. There are however common features in the care needs of 65 year olds with a circulation or heart complaint, of 75 year olds with arthritic hip joints, and of 85 year olds who are severely weakened by an endocrine or blood disorder. All make above-average demands in time and diagnostic skills of the general practitioner, all require extended and often multiple medication, many require the specialist knowledge and treatments of a hospital consultant, and many require convalescent, continuing or long-term care that involves the community health services, social services and residential care.

The commonality among them is that effective care requires high-quality liaison among several health and social care professionals and services. Prompt, clear, comprehensive and comprehensible communication is a vital element of treatment and care. This may be the norm and reports to the contrary may be unrepresentative – we simply do not know.

Clinicians and other staff do however report that many hospitals are operating under considerable pressures of patient demand, which leads too often to the 'crisis management' of individual conditions and few opportunities to assess the 'whole patient'. No routine source provides other than tangential information about the relative frequency of the occasions when condition-specific treatment has inappropriately failed to be informed by concurrent courses of care. No routine source collects data on the important inter-sectoral aspects of current provision. When so little is known about what is working well and what is working poorly, the success of even the most lavish investments could be low.

The clear information requirement is for the collection and collation of information about the performance of the key linkages in the system. London's community health councils and a previous King's Fund report have identified the need (Martin *et al.*, 1992). There should be data on the referral patterns and their outcomes for various conditions and by locality in the form of 'transition matrices' among the sectors of care and agencies. The data will be complex, with several 'origins' and 'destinations' and various intermediate providers of care, and with the additional complexities of variable episode and treatment intervals. The challenging design tasks, for both data collection and database architecture, should however be faced. The size, complexity and sophistication of the NHS should be matched by management and customer information of commensurate quality. The present blindness to system performance is a scandal.

There is always reluctance in an organisation to collect information that is not of immediate management value. One demonstration is the low participation of London's GPs in the decennial surveys initiated by their own Royal College. It will be important to avoid unwieldy and burdensome inquiries, but much harm will be done to the reputation of the service and to patients if we continue to be so ill-equipped to monitor and evaluate the services.

It is believed that a rigorously designed 'customer-based' standing inquiry across all health and social services could be established at a justifiable cost. The intricacy of the data requirements suggest that the principal source should not be routine operational data. The problems of ensuring consistency and reliability across a wide range of providers are probably too great. The emphasis should be on data quality not quantity, which also points towards the use of specially trained data-entry staff.

5 Community care assessments and purchasing

As in the rest of the country, a leading current cause of concern in the field of health and social welfare services for older people is the uneven and, in places, lamentable progress with the implementation of the Griffiths-inspired reforms in community care introduced in April 1993. The reforms have stimulated an immense literature. Useful recent digests include the commissioned reports for this study by Howse and Dalley (1996) and Challis and Pearson (1996), and the introductory chapter and other contributions to Phillips and Penhale (1996). There has also been research with a focus on Greater London (Lewis and Glennerster, 1996).

Under the NHS and Community Care Act 1990, care assessments, the design of care packages and purchasing was to be the responsibility of social service departments. On the other hand, their established role as direct providers of residential and domiciliary care was to be reduced by the withdrawal of central government grants. In practice, there have been long delays to the assessments, creating problems with the discharge of patients for acute trusts. There has been insufficient finance to support care plans. The new system was set in place with antediluvian forms of inter-professional communication and of patient/client monitoring. The problems in London have been exacerbated by too few independent and private sector residential and nursing home places, particularly in the inner boroughs. The city's institutional complexity has been heightened for this particular service by the polarised political ideologies of adjacent boroughs in inner London (a complication faced by no other English city although all can find tensions between the elected representatives and the professional staff). Some boroughs have been keen to encourage the privatisation of domiciliary and residential care; others have taken all opportunities to resist or delay. Overall, there has been too little money and too few staff, too weak an implementation strategy and too few residential places, and some obdurate and ideologically-grounded resistance. As a result placements have either not occurred or they have been taken on by hospital consultants, general practitioners, social workers and family members.

Linda Challis and Joanne Pearson (1996) have reviewed and analysed the community care plans (CCP) produced for 1995–96 and or 1996–97 by all but three of the London boroughs' social service departments, as well as 36 annual reports, business plans and primary care plans of NHS agencies in London. 'The CCPs paint a picture of authorities which are well aware of the significance of the mixed economy (of care) in matters of service provision or, to put it another way, the link between resource distribution and the service route to needs-identification' (ibid.). 'Assessing need from a service perspective is a strong feature of the plans', but it is also apparent that service planning is firmly guided by the Government's policy which requires 'a move from residential and institutional care to care within people's own homes.'

Two extracts illustrate the shift. The Kensington CCP states that, 'during 1995–96 there have been marked changes in the demand for domiciliary care. Increasing numbers of older people have been supported in their own homes. Expenditure on domiciliary care increased by 28 per cent with a further 6 per cent increase anticipated during 1996–97.' The level of service provided to individuals has also significantly increased, by 15 per cent in the number of people receiving more than five hours per week of care at home, and by 100 per cent in the number of people receiving live-in or overnight care in their homes (ibid.). From Southwark, 'there is a continuing increase in demand for home-based community care packages as an alternative to care in a residential environment.'

Challis and Pearson (1996) identify an 'economical approach to assessment' in several boroughs. 'In Camden there is a selective needs assessment team which carries out assessments when needs are likely to be met through a single service, for example home care, meals service, day care, or a combination. The team was initially established as a pilot and is staffed by a multi-agency team of seven assessors from Home Care, Age Concern, Camden Citizens' Advice Bureau and the Camden and Islington Community Health Services NHS Trust's Health Advisor for Elderly People. Multi-disciplinary assessment and care management teams from the health and social services have been established in local health centres, which provide a quick and responsive service for older people with complex needs (ibid.). They conclude by identifying several impediments to the implementation of community care management, which are interpreted as follows:

- problems within the boroughs in adopting consistent approaches to the identification and quantification of need;
- the absence of any mechanism for encouraging consistent or comparable methods and procedures among all boroughs;
- a general inability to find relevant population data for planning purposes and to translate the information into demand projections for different types of service;
- an unwillingness or inability to break away from present service configurations to enable innovation in service organisation and delivery;
- an incapacity to handle and reconcile data from different agencies or with different definitions and structures, and for the most part insufficient data skills to design the simplest counts of inter-sectoral flows.

The overall outcome in London as a whole is that the NHS and SSDs are delivering sub-optimal care to a most needy and vulnerable group of patients. The failings of 'care-management' have contributed to the raised anxiety and sense of abandonment among older people seen during the mid-1990s, and have done no good to the reputation of NHS and the statutory services. Possibly the ambition was too high. The bureaucratic complexity of keeping up with each client's changing needs has played a part in producing a totally confused and seemingly directionless picture. But the main problem is that the Griffiths proposals were enacted reluctantly and half-heartedly. The distinction between a free market in health and social care and the institutional and professional maze 'on the ground' was not confronted. No agency, not even a single Department of State, had overall responsibility for forcing the implementation through. The sticks and the carrots have been weak and readily avoided.

Weighty corroboration of many of these assessments is found in the Health Advisory Service's report *Addressing the Balance* (Health Advisory Service, 1997). It has examined closely the multi-disciplinary assessment of older people and the delivery of continuing care across the country. It argues that despite the good intentions of commissioners and providers, 'older people with complex needs are falling through the cracks between agencies. Services are fragmented, there are problems with funding, a lack of proper assessment and reassessment, inequity, and inadequate communication' (quoted in Millar, 1997). The report's overall view is that while services 'are by no means in a parlous state', the purchaser-provider split has created 'perverse incentives and unwelcome boundaries to communication and to the seamless delivery of care'. Among the more serious obstacles, it argues, is GP fundholding which has 'fragmented the purchasing role, dispersed the financial resources of health authorities and denuded them of personnel'. The HAs encountered problems between health and social services agencies, mostly concerned with the funding of long-term and continuing care, which led to difficult relationships. It also found that, where separated hospital and community trusts provided a range of health care services for older people, they were not working to achieve seamlessness in the provision of care. Richard Williams, immediate-past director of the HAS, has stated that 'what is needed is holistic, multi-disciplinary assessment at a number of different stages, a process that, as far as possible, involves GPs and primary health-care teams, 'care of the elderly' team specialists, social workers, health visitors, care managers and informal carers – a process that demands rigorous and inspired collaboration between those different elements' (quoted in Millar, 1997).

6 Multi-agency collaboration: strengths, limitations and improvement

Several references have been made to the many examples in London of individual providing agencies and groups of professionals being willing to work co-operatively and to engage in joint commissioning and funding. Bilateral and local arrangements often work well. They are not however working to a template and they are dependent upon goodwill. It is bound to be the case that some will have problems 'seeing the wood for the trees'. It may seem uncharitable, but there is an absurdity in so many hard-pressed and highly trained providers and managers having to devise from first principles the mechanisms for implementing community care 'from the grass-roots up', however laudable the effort and however imaginative and suited to local conditions the result. The structures and financial arrangements should have been in place from the start. The fall from the high ideals of Griffiths has dismaying bathos. If we read between the lines of the annual reports and local plans which express wholehearted commitment to joint working and detail the local experiments, the picture is frankly one of tokenism and of widespread strains on resources, facilities and staff. Whether tinkering will ever be sufficient is doubtful. 'Care of the elderly' services require a well-designed and integrated system, but we have a cottage industry of local initiatives.

The case for a fresh start to the implementation of care-management is clear. The delegation of the system-design function to individual providers and *ad hoc* consortia must be ended. Instead, it should be recognised that the exceptional organisational difficulties of successful 'community care' will only achieve an acceptable level of output, equity and efficiency with the use of a flexible template and detailed implementation (and training) strategies. The template could be designed without excessive delay by drawing on the wealth of community care research and by identifying good practice among the current local arrangements. Actual care pathways, shared responsibilities and provider roles must all be established. The legal, financial and professional frameworks for joint working must be thought through, designed and piloted. The system will have to be 'engineered' into place, so pilots (of say six months) might be valuable.

The tactical position in London is that following the primary care initiatives of the last few years, the next priority is in the field of the community health and personal social services. The wider agenda will include tackling the variability of community health and social service provision. The variability would be critically appraised, following which specific initiatives to 'level-up' would be taken. Another task would be to understand further the high costs of community and social care in London and, following studies and experiments (probably in the areas of staff recruitment, training, grading and retention), to propose measures for their reduction. The most ambitious and exciting element of a community health and social service initiative would however be to take on the pilot (but substantial) exercise to rejuvenate and complete the implementation of 'community care'. The experiment would have national significance.

The ambition should however go beyond the 'care of the elderly' services for the most frail and dependent older people. The further challenge is to establish effective mechanisms for monitoring, evaluating and managing the complex treatment pathways of acute episodes as well as the treatment and care of those with high requirements for health and social care. The remit would be to tackle health care delivery to all age-groups, but the process might usefully begin with older patients. The medium term goal should be to establish not only the effective audit of multi-provider and inter-sectoral care but also effective powers and mechanisms to correct sub-optimal treatment and care 'routing' and outcomes. Undoubtedly the organisational and professional complexities are profound, but at the same time no sector or professional group has a vested interest in the perpetuation of the present unsatisfactory arrangements. Many experienced and able people will be found who will be highly motivated to engineer a radical solution into place.

7 Conclusion

Three issues of concern about the performance of the health and social services in London have persisted throughout this review. The large size and distinctiveness of the capital, particularly its unusual hospital provision, affect not only the availability of hospital services to older people but also appear to distort the provision made by other sectors. Secondly, the continuing deficiencies in the general medical services in inner London are a cause for concern, particularly with regard to the effective management of older patients' acute episodes, not least through 'after-care'. And thirdly, the multiplicity of providing units and agencies magnifies the endemic problems of liaison and communication within the service.

The greatest problem faced by this study has been the scarcity of information about even the most basic performance indicators on a *population or client basis* of London's health and welfare services for older people. This is itself a telling commentary on two aspects of the management and regulation of the NHS. The performance and productivity indicators have concentrated on throughput and outcome measures for individual providing units. These are inadequate tools with which to assess the quality and effectiveness of the NHS for any group of patients but particularly for those with chronic and multiple disorders.

One strong suggestion is that a concerted effort is made to improve the evaluation of the NHS and social service system of health and social care for older people in London. It is emphasised that the recommendation is not confined to the elaborate provision that has to be made for the very frail and dependent, it applies also to the larger number of patients experiencing acute episodes for which treatment and care is required from more than one service. The foundation for any evaluation is good data. It has been argued that for the purpose of appraising the performance of the health and social service system as a whole, a new source is required, not confined to existing operational data but developing patient-based longitudinal records of their contacts of all kinds. Many of the issues that prevail in this report are highlighted in the issue of 'community care'. All reports concur that the arrangements have been haphazardly and unevenly applied and are not working well. Four years from introduction, some slow improvements are reported, but unless a radical approach to the task is undertaken, one suspects that community care will never be better than 'making do'. A widespread enthusiasm to make improvements and to work collaboratively has been shown. The changed national government and the imminence of a new elected authority for London presents a wonderful and politically-expedient opportunity to take a major stride towards seamless care.

Geographical classifications

Sectors of London

District Health Authorities

North West
Kensington, Chelsea & Westminster
Ealing, Hammersmith & Hounslow
Brent & Harrow
Hillingdon

North Central
Camden & Islington
Enfield & Haringey
Barnet

East
East London & the City
Redbridge & Waltham Forest
Barking & Havering

South East
Lambeth, Southwark & Lewisham
Bexley & Greenwich
Bromley

South
Merton, Sutton & Wandsworth
Kingston & Richmond
Croydon

Socio-Economic Areas

London District Health Authorities

Inner-deprived
Kensington, Chelsea & Westminster
East London & the City
Camden & Islington
Lambeth, Southwark & Lewisham

Mixed-status
Brent & Harrow
Ealing, Hammersmith
  & Hounslow
Redbridge & Waltham Forest
Enfield & Haringey
Merton, Sutton & Wandsworth

High-status
Barnet
Hillingdon
Barking & Havering
Bromley
Bexley & Greenwich
Croydon
Kingston & Richmond

London Local Authorities

Inner-deprived
City of London
Hackney
Tower Hamlets
Newham
Camden
Islington
Kensington and Chelsea
City of Westminster
Lambeth
Southwark
Lewisham

Mixed-status
Ealing
Hammersmith and Fulham
Hounslow
Brent
Harrow
Enfield
Haringey
Redbridge
Waltham Forest
Merton
Sutton
Wandsworth

High-status
Hillingdon
Barnet
Barking
Havering
Kingston upon Thames
Richmond upon Thames
Croydon
Greenwich
Bexley
Bromley

Non-London District Health Authorities

Inner-deprived	**Mixed-status**	**High-status**
Sunderland	North Durham	Nottingham
South of Tyne	South Durham	Cambridge
Newcastle & North Tyneside	Tees	Huntingdon
Bradford	Grimsby & Scunthorpe	Bedfordshire
Leeds	West Yorkshire	North West Hertfordshire
Sheffield	Wakefield	South West Hertfordshire
South Birmingham	Southern Derbyshire	East & North Hertfordshire
Liverpool	Leicestershire	North Essex
Manchester	Barnsley	South Essex
	Doncaster	East Kent
Non-London combined DHAs	Rotherham	West Kent
North Birmingham:	North Nottinghamshire	East Surrey
64% Inner-deprived, 36% High-status	North Staffordshire	Mid-Downs
Salford & Trafford:	Coventry	North West Surrey
51% Inner-deprived, 49% High-status	Dudley	South West Surrey
Northamptonshire:	Sandwell	Mid-Surrey
45% Mixed-status, 55% High-status	Walsall	Portsmouth & SE Hampshire
Bury & Rochdale:	Wolverhampton	Southampton & SW Hampshire
46% Mixed-status, 54% High-status	North Cheshire	North & Mid Hampshire
	St Helens & Knowsley	Wiltshire & Bath
	Bolton	Berkshire
	Wigan	Buckinghamshire
	East Lancashire	Oxfordshire
	West Pennine	Bristol & District
		Gloucestershire
		Solihull
		North Worcestershire
		South Staffordshire
		Warwickshire
		Chester
		South East Cheshire
		Sefton
		Wirral
		Stockport

Appendix 2

Commissioned Papers for the Older People Programme

Health and Social Care Provision for London's Black and Minority Ethnic Older Population, Aanchawan T. (King's Fund) and Khan S. (University of Westminster)

Towards an Analysis of the Health and Social Care Needs of Older Londoners, Challis L. and Pearson J. (Oxford Brookes University)

Health Status and Health Care Utilisation among Elderly Persons in Britain, Evandrou M. (King's Fund)

The Demography of Older People in London, Hollis J. (London Research Centre)

A Review of Services for Older People in London, Howse K. and Dalley G. (Centre for Policy on Ageing)

Estimating Levels of Need among Older People in London, Kenny D. (London Research Centre)

Trends in Social Service Activity, Staffing and Expenditure in Relation to Older People in London, Kenny D. (London Research Centre)

Users' Views of Local Health Services for Older People in London, Mortimer K. (Centre for Policy on Ageing)

Summary of Commissioned Thematic Papers, Poxton R. (King's Fund)

Local Authority Financial Resources, Stanton R. and Brangwyn M. (Association of London Government)

Irish Older People in London, Tilki M. (Federation of Irish Societies and Middlesex University)

References

Abel-Smith, B. 1964. *The Hospitals 1800–1948.* London: Heinemann.

Alderson, M. 1975. Statistics as a basis for health management and planning. In: W.F. Maunder (ed), *Reviews of United Kingdom Statistical Sources,* volume 2, London: Heinemann.

Alderson, M. 1984. Health information resources: the United Kingdom. In: W.W. Holland (ed), *The Oxford Textbook of Public Health*, Oxford: Oxford University Press.

Alderson, M. 1988. Demographic and health trends in the elderly. In: N. Wells and C. Freer (eds), *The Ageing Population: Burden of Challenge.* Basingstoke: Macmillan, pp. 87–102.

Askham, J., Henshaw, L. and Tarpey, M. 1995. *Social and Health Authority Services for Older People from Black and Minority Ethnic Communities*, London: HMSO.

Audit Commission 1992. *Constructing Budgets for Purchasing Community Care,* London: District Audit Service, Audit Commission.

Bacon, V. and Lambkin, C. 1997. The relationship between the delivery of day care services for older people and the design of day care premises. *Ageing and Society,* 17: 41–64.

Badger, F., Atkin, K. and Griffiths, R. 1989. Why don't general practitioners refer their disabled Asian patients to district nurses? *Health Trends,* 21.

Balarajan, R. 1996. Ethnicity and variations in mortality from coronary disease. *Health Trends,* 28(2): 45–51.

Balarajan, R. and Bulusu, L. 1990. Mortality among immigrants in England and Wales, 1979-83. In: M. Britton (ed), *Mortality and Geography: A Review in the Mid-1980s,* OPCS DS 9, London: HMSO.

Banerjee, S. 1993. Prevalence and recognition rates of psychiatric-disorder in the elderly clients of a community care service. *International Journal of Geriatric Psychiatry,* 8(2):125–131.

Barker, D.J.P. 1992. The fetal origins of diseases of old age. *European Journal of Clinical Nutrition,* 46 (Supplement 3), S3-S9.

Barker, D.J.P. 1994. *Mothers, Babies and Disease in Later Life,* London: British Medical Journal Publishing.

Bebbington, A.C. 1991. The expectation of life without disability in England and Wales. *Population Trends,* 66:26–29.

Bebbington, A.C. 1995. Chapter 6 in Bone, M.R., Bebbington, A.C., Jagger, C., Morgan, K. and Nicolaas, G. *Health Expectancy and Its Uses.* London: HMSO.

Benzeval, M., Judge, K. and Solomon, M. 1992. *The Health Status of Londoners: A Comparative Perspective,* London: Commission on the Future of Acute Health Services in London, King's Fund.

Blackwell Masters Publishing 1997. *National Health Database.* Computer software database. Waterlooville, Hampshire: Blackwell Masters.

Blakemore, K. and Boneham, M. 1994. *Age, Race and Ethnicity: A Comparative Approach*, Buckingham: Open University Press.

Blanchard, M.R., Waterreus, A. and Mann, A.H. 1994. The nature of depression among older people in inner London, and the contact with primary care. *British Journal of Psychiatry,* 164:396–402.

Bone, M.R. 1995. *Trends in Dependency Among Older People in England,* London: Social Survey Division, OPCS.

Bone, M.R., Bebbington, A.C., Jagger, C., Morgan, K. and Nicolaas, G. 1995. *Health Expectancy and Its Uses.* London: HMSO.

Bowling, A. and Farquhar, M. 1993. The health and well-being of Jewish people aged 65 to 85 living at home in the East End of London. *Ageing and Society,* 13(2):213–45.

Boyle, S. and Hamblin, R. 1997. *The Health Economy of London,* London: London Commission Report, King's Fund.

Boyle, S. and Smaje, C. 1992. *Acute Health Services in London: An Analysis,* London: Commission on the Future of Acute Health Services in London, King's Fund.

Butler, J., Bevan, J.M. and Taylor, R. 1973. *Family Doctors and Public Policy,* London: Routledge & Kegan Paul.

Bytheway, W.R. 1995. *Ageism.* Buckingham: Open University Press.

Callahan, D. 1987. *Setting Limits: Medical Goals in an Aging Society*, New York: Simon & Schuster.

Callahan, D. 1990. *What Kind of Life: The Limits of Medical Progress,* New York: Simon & Schuster.

Carnegie UK Trust 1993. *Health, Abilities and Well-Being in the Third Age,* Dunfermline: Carnegie UK Trust.

Caselli, G. 1994. *Long-term Trends in European Mortality.* Studies on Medical and Population Subjects No. 56. London: Office of Population Censuses and Surveys.

Central Health Monitoring Unit 1992. *The Health of Elderly People: An Epidemiological Overview*, Volume 1 and Companion Papers. London: HMSO.

Challis, L. and Pearson, J. 1996. *Towards an analysis of the health and social care needs of older Londoners.* Study paper for the King's Fund London Commission Older People Programme. Oxford: School of Health Care Studies, Oxford Brookes University.

Charlton, J., Wallace, M. and White, I. 1994. Long-term illness: results from the 1991 census. *Population Trends*, 75:18–25.

Clark, H. 1996. *Going Home: Older People Leaving Hospital,* Bristol: Policy Press.

Coleman, D.A. (ed) 1982. *Demography of Immigrant and Minority Groups in the United Kingdom.* London: Academic.

Congdon, P. 1988. Deprivation in London wards: mortality and unemployment trends in the 1980s. *The Statistician,* 37:451–72.

Cribier, F. and Kych, A. 1993 A comparison of retirement migration from Paris and London. *Environment and Planning A,* 26:1399–1420.

Crimmins, E.M., Saito, Y. and Reynolds, S.L. 1997. Further evidence on recent trends in the prevalence and incidence of disability among older Americans from two sources: the LSOA and NHIS. *Journal of Gerontology: Social Sciences,* 52B(2): S59–S71.

Cunningham, D. 1983. *Overview of Psychiatric Services in London Health Districts.* Paper presented to King's Fund Conference on Issues for London DHAs: The Development of Psychiatric Services.

Curran, J.S.M. 1996. The evolution of day care services for people with dementia. In: R. Bland (ed), *Developing Services for Older People and Their Families,* London: Jessica Kingsley, pp. 112–28.

Daykin, C.D. 1994. The recent trend of mortality in the United Kingdom. *Journal of the Institute of Actuaries* 121(3): 589–96.

Department of Health and Social Security (DHSS) 1981. *Primary Care in Inner London,* (The Acheson Report), London: DHSS.

DHSS 1986. *Primary Health Care: An Agenda for Discussion,* Cmnd 9771, London: HMSO.

Department of Health (DH) 1989. *Caring for People: Community Care in the Next Decade and Beyond.* Cmnd 849. London: HMSO.

DH 1990. *Community Care in the Next Decade and Beyond: Policy Guidance.* London: HMSO.

DH 1993. *Implementing Caring for People: Assessment.* Letter to London Directors of Social Services, 1 March, London: DH.

DH 1995. Memorandum. In House of Commons, Health Committee, Sessions 1994-95, *Minutes of Evidence, 11 May 1995.* London: HMSO.

Department of the Environment 1995. *1991 Deprivation Index: A Review of Approaches and a Matrix of Results.* London: HMSO.

Diamond, I. and Clarke, S. 1989. Demographic patterns among Britain's ethnic groups. In: Joshi, H. (ed.), *The Changing Population of Britain*, Oxford: Basil Blackwell, pp. 177–98.

Dudley, N.J. and Burns, E. 1992. The influence of age on policies for admission and thrombolysis in coronary care units in the United Kingdom. *Age and Ageing,* 21: 95–8.

Eade, J., Vamplew, T. and Peach, C. 1996. The Bangladeshis: the encapsulated community. In C. Peach (ed.), *Ethnicity in the Census. Volume 2: The Ethnic Minority Populations of Great Britain.* London: HMSO, pp. 150–60.

Ebrahim, S. 1992. Health and ageing within ethnic minorities. In: Morgan, K. (ed) *Gerontology: Responding to an Ageing Society*, London: Jessica Kingsley, pp. 50–62.

Ebrahim, S., Patel, N. and Coats, M. 1991. Prevalence and severity of morbidity among Gujarati Asian elderly: a controlled comparison. *Family Practice*, 8, 57–62.

Evandrou, M. 1997. *Health status and health care utilisation among elderly persons in Britain.* Briefing paper for the London Commission. London: King's Fund Policy Institute.

Evans, J.G. 1994. Gestation, growth and old age vulnerability. *Ageing and Society,* 14 (1):123–26.

Evans, J.G. 1997. The clinical achievements of British geriatrics. In: J. Phillips (ed) *British Gerontology and Geriatrics,* London: BGS/BSRA/BSG, pp. 5–12.

Eversley, D.E.C. 1982. The demography of retirement. In: M.P. Fogarty (ed), *Retirement Policy: The Next Fifty Years,* London: Heinemann, pp. 14–40.

Fox, J. and Goldblatt, P.O. 1982. *OPCS Longitudinal Study, 1971-75: Socio-Demographic Mortality Differentials,* OPCS Series LS No. 1, London: HMSO.

Fox, J., Jones, D., Moser, K. and Goldblatt, P. 1985. Socio-demographic differentials in mortality. *Population Trends*, 40, 10–16.

Freer, C. 1988. Old myths: frequent misconceptions about the elderly. In: N. Wells and C. Freer (eds), *The Ageing Population: Burden or Challenge.* Basingstoke: Macmillan, pp. 3–15

Griffiths, R. 1988. *Community Care: Agenda for Action.* London: HMSO.

Grundy, E. 1992a. Socio-demographic change. In: Central Monitoring Unit, *The Health of Older People: An Epidemiological Overview,* London: HMSO.

Grundy E. 1992b. The epidemiology of aging. In: Brocklehurst J.C., Tallis, R. and Fillit, H. (eds), *Textbook of Geriatric Medicine and Gerontology.* Edinburgh: Churchill Livingstone.

Hall, M. 1988. Geriatric medicine today. In: N. Wells and C. Freer (eds), *The Ageing Population: Burden or Challenge.* Basingstoke: Macmillan, pp. 65–86.

Hall, P.G. 1989. *London 2001.* London: Heinemann.

Hamnett, C. and Mullings, B. 1992. The distribution of public and private residential homes for older persons in England and Wales. *Area*, 24(2), pp. 130–44.

Harrison, A. 1997. *The London Health Care System,* London: King's Fund.

Health Advisory Service 1997. *Addressing the Balance,* London: HMSO.

Hofman, A., Rocca, W.A., Brayne, C. *et al.* 1991. The prevalence of vascular dementia in Europe – facts and fragments from 1980–1990 studies, *Annals of Neurology,* 30(6):817–824.

Howse, K. and Dalley, G. 1996. A review of services for older people in London. Study Paper for the King's Fund London Commission Older People Programme. London: Centre for Policy on Ageing.

Iliffe, S, Booroff, A., Gallivan, S., Goldenberg, E. and Morgan P. 1991a. Assessment of older people in general practice. Part 1: Social circumstances and mental state. *British Journal of General Practice,* 41:459–61.

Iliffe, S, Booroff, A., Gallivan, S., Goldenberg, E., Morgan P. and Gallivan, S. 1991b. Alcohol consumption by older people: a general practice survey. *Age and Ageing,* 20:120–23.

Jarman, B. 1981. *A Survey of Primary Care in London.* Occasional Paper 16, London: Royal College of General Practitioners.

Johnson, S. *et al.* 1997. *London's Mental Health,* London: London Commission Report, King's Fund.

Johnson, S., Ramsay, R. and Thornicroft, G. 1997. Londoners' mental health needs: the socio-demographic context. In: Johnson, S. *et al., op. cit.,* pp. 15–32.

Jones, E. 1991. Race and ethnicity in London. In: K. Hoggart and D.R. Green (eds), *London: A New Metropolitan Geography*, London: Arnold, pp. 176–190.

Jorm, A. 1990. *The Epidemiology of Alzheimer's Disease and Related Disorders,* London: Chapman & Hall.

Judge, K. and Solomon, M. 1993. Public opinion and the NHS: patterns and perspectives in consumer satisfaction. *Journal of Social Policy,* 22(3): 299–327.

Kendrick, A. and Warnes, A.M. 1997. The demography and mental health of older people. In: I.J. Norman and S.J. Redfern (eds), *Mental Health Care for Older People,* Edinburgh: Churchill Livingstone, pp. 3–20.

Kenny, D. 1996a. *Estimating Levels of Need Among Older People in London.* Report for the King's Fund London Commission. London: London Research Centre.

Kenny, D. 1996b. *Trends in Social Services Activity, Staffing and Expenditure in Relation to Older People in London.* London: London Research Centre.

King's Fund Commission on the Future of Acute Health Services in London 1992. *London Health Care 2010: Changing the Future of Services in the Capital,* London: King's Fund.

Koffman, J. 1997. *A Survey of the District Nursing Service in Riverside Community Health Care NHS Trust, 11 February 1997.* London: Department of Public Health, Kensington & Chelsea and Westminster Health Authority.

Levin, E., Moriarty, J. and Gorbach, P. 1994. 'Day care'. In: *Better for the Break.* London: HMSO.

Lewis, J. and Glennerster, H. 1996. *Implementing the New Community Care,* Buckingham: Open University Press.

Lindesay, J. 1991. Anxiety disorders in the elderly. In: Jacoby, R. and Oppenheimer, C. (eds), *Psychiatry in the Elderly,* Oxford: Oxford University Press.

Lindesay, J., Briggs, K. and Murphy, E. 1989. The Guy's/Age Concern Survey: prevalence rates of cognitive impairment, depression and anxiety in an urban elderly community. *British Journal of Psychiatry,* 155:17–329.

London Health Planning Consortium 1981. *Primary Health Care in Inner London.* London: LHPC.

Maheswaran, R., Elliott, P. and Strachan, D.P. 1997. Socio-economic deprivation, ethnicity and stroke mortality in Greater London and South East England, *Journal of Epidemiology and Community Health,* 51 (2): 127–31.

Maheswaran, R., Strachan, D.P., Elliott, P. and Shipley, M.J. 1997. Trends in stroke mortality in Greater London and South East England: evidence for a cohort effect? *Journal of Epidemiology and Community Health,* 51(2): 121–6.

Manton, K., Corder, L. and Stallard, E. 1997. Chronic disability trends in elderly United States populations, 1982–1994, *Proceedings of the National Academy of Sciences,* 94(6): 2593–8.

Martin, P., Wiles, R., Pratten, B., Gorton, S. and Green, J. 1992. *A User Perspective: Views on London's Acute Health Services.* Report for the Commission on the Future of Acute Services in London. London: King's Fund.

Maxwell, R. 1993. Other cities, same problems. In: J. Smith (ed), *London After Tomlinson: Reorganising Big City Medicine.* London: BMJ Publishing, pp. 101–7.

McCalman, J.A. 1990. *The Forgotten People: Carers in Three Ethnic Minority Communities in Southwark*, London: King's Fund Centre.

McCormick, A. and Rosenbaum, M. 1990. *Morbidity Statistics from General Practice: The Third National Study: Socio-Economic Analysis.* London: HMSO.

McCormick, A., Fleming, D. and Charlton, J. 1995. *Morbidity Statistics from General Practice: The Fourth National Study 1992-1992.* OPCS Series MB5 No. 3. London: HMSO.

Medical Research Council 1994. *The Health of the UK's Elderly People: Topic Review.* London: MRC.

Millar, B. 1997. Falling between the cracks. *Health Service Journal,* 27 March, 13.

Mohan, J. 1989. Health care policy issues. In: D.T. Herbert and D.M. Smith (eds), *Social Problems and the City,* Oxford: Oxford University Press, pp. 126–41.

Moody, H. 1988. *Abundance of Life: Human Development Policies for an Ageing Society.* New York: Columbia University Press.

Moody, H. 1995. Ageing, meaning and the allocation of resources. *Ageing and Society,* 15: 163–84.

Mortimer, K. 1996. *Users' Views of Local Health Services for Older People in London.* Report for the King's Fund London Commission. London: Centre for Policy on Ageing.

Murphy, E. 1982. Social origins of depression in old age. *British Journal of Psychiatry.* 141: 135–42.

Neuberger, J. 1993. Community health services. In: J. Smith (ed.), *London After Tomlinson: Reorganising Big City Medicine.* London: BMJ Publishing, pp. 54–62.

Office for National Statistics 1997. *Mortality Statistics 1993: Area.* Series DH5. London: HMSO.

Office of Population Censuses and Surveys (OPCS) 1979. *Morbidity Statistics from General Practice 1971–2. Second National Study.* London: HMSO.

OPCS 1982. *Census of Great Britain 1981: Greater London.* CR17, London: HMSO.

OPCS 1988-89. *Surveys of Disability in Great Britain,* Reports 1-4, London: HMSO.

OPCS 1989. *Mortality Statistics 1841-1985, Serial Tables,* London: HMSO.

OPCS 1993a. *Great Britain 1991 Census: Ethnic Group and Country of Birth.* 2 vols. London: HMSO.

OPCS 1993b. *National Population Projections: 1991-Based,* Series PP2, No. 18, London: HMSO.

OPCS 1994a. *Mortality Statistics 1992, England and Wales, General,* London: HMSO.

OPCS 1994b. *Mortality Statistics 1992, England and Wales, Area,* London: HMSO.

OPCS 1995. *Morbidity Statistics from General Practice 1991-2. Fourth National Study.* London: HMSO.

Organisation for Economic Co-operation and Development (OECD) 1990. *Health Care Systems in Transition,* Paris: OECD.

Owen, D. 1996. Size, structure and growth of the minority ethnic populations. In: D. Coleman and J. Salt (eds), *Ethnicity in the 1991 Census: Demographic Characteristics of the Ethnic Minority Populations.* London: HMSO, pp. 151–77.

Pharoah, C. 1995. *Primary Care for Older People from Black and Minority Ethnic Minorities,* London: HMSO.

Philpot, M. and Banerjee, S. 1997. Mental health services for older people in London. In: Johnson, S. *et al.* (eds), *London's Mental Health,* London: King's Fund London Commission, pp. 46–62.

Phillips, J. and Penhale, B. (eds) 1996. *Reviewing Care Management for Older People,* London: Jessica Kingsley.

Powell, M. 1987. Territorial justice and primary health care: an example from London. *Social Science and Medicine* 24, 1093–103.

Richards, M. 1997. Anxiety in later life. In: I.J. Norman and S.J. Redfern (eds), *Mental Health Care for Older people,* Edinburgh: Churchill Livingstone, pp. 131–40.

Rivett, G. 1986. *The Development of the London Hospital System,* London: King's Fund.

Royal College of Physicians 1977. *Working Party Report on Care of the Elderly,* London: Royal College of Physicians.

Royal College of Physicians 1994. *Ensuring Equity and Quality of Care for Elderly People: The Interface between Geriatric Medicine and General (Internal) Medicine,* London: Royal College of Physicians.

Royal College of Physicians 1995. *Setting Priorities in the NHS: A Framework for Decision-Making,* London: Royal College of Physicians.

Royal Commission on the National Health Service. 1979. *Report of the Royal Commission on the NHS*, London: HMSO.

Russell, J., Petterson, G. and Davies, G. 1994. *Londoners' Views on the Future of Health Care*. Report for the Commission on the Future of Acute Services in London. London: King's Fund.

Social Services Inspectorate 1991. *Care Management and Practitioners' Guide*, London: HMSO.

Stevenson, O. 1996. Changing practice: professional attitudes, consumerism and empowerment. In: R. Bland (ed), *Developing Services for Older People and Their Families*, London: Jessica Kingsley, pp. 204–14.

Stillwell, J., Rees, P. and Duke-Williams, O. 1996. Migration between NUTS Level 2 Regions in the United Kingdom. In: Rees, P., Stillwell, J., Coney A. and Kupiszewski, M. (eds), *Population Migration in the European Union*, Chichester: Wiley, pp. 275–310.

Storkey, M. and Lewis, R. 1996. London: a true cosmopolis. In: P. Radcliffe (ed), *Ethnicity in the Census. Volume 3: Social Geography and Ethnicity in Britain: Geographical Spread, Spatial Concentration and Internal Migration.* London: HMSO, pp. 201–25.

Stuart, A. 1987. Migration and population turnover in a London Borough: the incidence and implications of retirement out-migration. *Espaces Populations Sociétés* 1987/1, pp. 137–51.

Swift, C. 1989. Health care of the elderly: the concept of progress. In: A. Warnes (ed), *Human Ageing and Later Life,* London: Arnold, pp. 135-145.

Thomas, B. 1962. *The Welsh Economy: Studies in Expansion.* Aberystwyth: University of Wales Press.

Tilki, M. 1996. *Older Irish People in London.* London: Federation of Irish Societies and University of Middlesex.

Tinker, A. 1992. *Elderly People in Modern Society*, third edition, London: Longman, chapter 6.

Tomlinson, B. 1992. *Report of the Inquiry into London's Health Services, Medical Education and Research.* London: HMSO.

United Nations Organisation 1993. *Demographic Yearbook 1993: Special Issue, Population Aging and the Situation of Elderly Persons.* New York: UNO.

Victor, C.R. 1996. Broken down by age and sex: an examination of old age in the inner city. In: D. Guez (ed) *Home Care,* Paris: Serdi, pp. 85–101.

Walker, A. and Maltby, T. 1997. *Ageing Europe.* Buckingham: Open University Press.

Walker, R. and Ahmed, W. 1994. Asian and Black elders and community care: a survey of care providers. *New Community*, 20 (4):635–46.

Warnes, A.M. 1991. London's population trends: megalopolis or metropolitan area. In: K. Hoggart and D.R. Green (eds), *London: A New Metropolitan Geography*, London: Arnold, pp. 156–75.

Warnes, A.M. 1994. Cities and elderly people: recent population and distributional trends. *Urban Studies,* 31 (4/5): 799–816.

Warnes, A.M. 1996a. The age structure and ageing of the ethnic groups. In: D.C. Coleman and J. Salt (eds), *Ethnicity in the 1991 Census. Volume 1: Demographic Characteristics of the Minority Ethnic Populations,* pp. 151–77, London: HMSO.

Warnes, A.M. 1996b. *Demographic ageing and late-age mortality trends in Europe,* Report for the European Commission DGXII-E-4 Project *SCOPE.* Sheffield: Centre for Ageing and Rehabilitation Studies, University of Sheffield.

Warnes, A.M. and Ford, R. 1995. Housing aspirations and migration in later life: developments during the 1980s. *Papers in Regional Science,* 74(4), 361–87.

Warnes, A.M., Armstrong, G., Peters, D., Philp. I. and Power, J. 1995. *Age, Deprivation and Needs for Health and Social Services Among Elderly People in Eastern Northern Ireland,* Report to Eastern Health and Social Services Board, Belfast. Sheffield: Department of Health Care for Elderly People, University of Sheffield.

Warren, M.W. 1943. Care of chronic sick: a case for treating chronic sick in blocks in general hospital. *British Medical Journal,* ii, 822–3.

Warren, M.W. 1946. Care of the chronic aged sick. *Lancet,* I: 841–3.

Whitehead, M. 1987. *The Health Divide: Inequalities in Health in the 1980s,* London: Health Education Council.

Wistow, G. and Hardy, B. 1994. Community care planning. In: N. Malin (ed), *Implementing Community Care,* Buckingham: Open University Press, pp. 45–58.

Wood, J. 1983. Are the problems of primary care in inner cities fact or fiction? *BMJ* 286, 1249–52.

Young, E., Wallace, P. and Bruster, S. 1993. *Link-working,* London: Helen Hamlyn Foundation.